Coming Out of Darkness

A Family's Journey
Through Mental Illness

By Teresa A. Tate

Acclaim for
Coming Out of Darkness

"Simply a must read for those struggling with what to do and how to support their loved ones with mental illness. This book discusses vital suggestions for how to support loved ones through their mental health recovery. With her great insight, Author Teresa Tate has been able to provide a detailed account, through the use of real people's perspectives and situations, of what it's like to traverse the highs and lows of caring for a loved one with a mental health condition. Nobody talks about mental illness in ways that are as illuminating and compelling as Teresa."

Dr. Aaron Givens, Ph.D., LMHC
Certified Mental Health Instructor
Mental and Behavioral Health Consultant
Aaron Givens and Associates, LLC

"This practical book offers a wonderful framework for the mental health professional, and it brings new hope for family members who strive to find the best solution for those that they love. It is obvious that the authors know both worlds intimately, which brings comfort to the reader, as they walk through the world of mental illness. This book will give you the ability to 'see' right through a complicated and confusing epidemic that faces our world today and to tackle it head on. It truly does offer a straightforward approach that gets to the heart of the issue with helpful sound advice."

Kathleen D. Mailer
Founder of ChristianAuthorsGetPaid.com
Co-Founder of Iron Sharpens Iron Ministries
International Business Evangelist
#1 Best Selling Author (*Walking In the Wake of the Holy Spirit*,
Living an Ordinary Life with an Extraordinary God)

"*Coming Out of Darkness: A Family's Journey Through Mental Illness* illuminates the myriad experiences and challenges associated with supporting a loved one with mental illness. This collaborative book project is well-researched and sensitively written, and it takes the reader into the hearts of family members who have given their all to support their loved ones with mental illness. Each chapter reflects an authentic and transparent personal journey, and infused into each page is the love of these family members for their loved ones. Despite their ups and downs, the authors skillfully marshalled their supports and resources to ensure a successful outcome for their families and loved ones, without getting forever lost in the dark. If you are dealing with a loved one with mental illness, make this book your lifeline of hope and encouragement as well as your step-by-step guide on how to navigate challenges incurred along this road. I am grateful for this most important book!"

Ms. Leslie J. Smith, B.A., LL.B.
Canadian Employment Lawyer, Mediator,
Small Claims Court Judge
Author of *Legal Ease: Essential Legal Strategies to Protect Canadian Non-union Employees* &
Without Excuse: Saying "NO!" to Relational Recklessness
www.lesliejsmithlaw.com. www.withoutexcusebook.ca

"Based on her own experiences, Teresa Tate illustrates the challenges of caring for a child with mental illness in a way no one else can. She shares the societal pressures, the navigation, and the difficult decisions she had to make. This accumulation of practical experiences and recommendations provides insights and directions on how to lovingly care for your loved one without stigma. This collaborative book project will inspire honest conversations and hope to those on a similar journey. This is required reading for anyone who has a child or loved one with mental health challenges."

Dr. Jeannice Fairrer Samani, PhD., MBA, MED
Information Technologist, Professor, & Speaker

"Coming Out of Darkness: A Family's Journey Through Mental Illness is a powerful account of family members who have begun to deal with the realities of having a loved one with mental illness. It not only deals with the practical and emotional concerns of having a loved one with a mental health diagnosis, but it also gives solutions and ideas for dealing with the plethora of issues that arise when supporting your loved one. Mental health issues are ever-present and a growing challenge in our lives, but they also provide an awesome opportunity for God to show Himself mightily. The fact that no one is exempt from coping with the realities of mental illness is a humbling reminder, and this compilation of memoirs is an opportunity for us to see ourselves in these experiences as well as to broaden our own repertoire in dealing with mental health issues in a manner that is real, healthy, and encouraging. This collaborative book project is needed NOW so that we can heal our loved ones, families, and communities."

Elder Leilah K. Kirkendoll, PhD
City of Hope International Church

"For far too long mental health concerns have gone unrecognized, untreated, and otherwise demonized in the Christian church. As a Pastor and wife team who both have experience in recognizing and treating mental health issues, we understand the importance of exposing mental illness and debunking the myth that mental illness is synonymous with demon possession. Pastor Teresa Tate takes us on a journey to find emotional and spiritual healing, not just for her son, but for the entire family. Tate's willingness to be transparent is yet another step toward holistic healing for Christian families."

Pastor Tobaise Brookins
Senior Pastor, Bethesda Churches of Fresno, California
Antionette D. Brookins, MS
Licensed Marriage and Family Therapist

"In families all over the world, mental illness is often the unspoken and forbidden topic that brings guilt, shame, and helplessness to everyone involved. Mental illness is a disease that is unmerited and unpredictable, and it has taunted families regardless of status, occupation, or educational accomplishments.

Coming Out of Darkness is a must read! You are guaranteed to be inspired by this account of a family's frantic attempt to intervene on behalf of a loved one with mental illness. Out of the womb of experience, this collaborative book project illustrates how the family unit rose to the occasion to support a loved one undergoing a mental health crisis. Love provoked each of them to go the extra mile in their own special way. Through the anguish of making tough decisions, their unwavering example of love was the catalyst for change. It took a village to get through this life crisis.

As I read this heart-wrenching journey, I discovered tools to assist those who battle life-altering circumstances, including mental illness, addictions, and life's hardships. Ultimately, this book shows the grace of God woven throughout the fabrics of their lives. I could clearly see that God extends His loving hands to anyone who is battling mental illness."

Dr. Tanda Joy Canion
Author of *Blood on the Floor: A Story of Grace and Hope*,
Cooking with Tanda Canion, & *Daily Dose of the Word*
Founder, Tanda Canion Ministries &
Tanda Canion Foundation
Pastor, Assembly of Truth Family Worship Center

Coming Out of Darkness: A Family's Journey Through Mental Illness

Edited by Natalie N. Watson-Singleton, PhD

ISBN: 978-0-9994078-8-2
Printed in the United States of America.
Registered with the Library of Congress.

Cover Designed by Lameisha Sherri | Zanie Creations
Manufactured in the United States of America

Publishing Info and Address: Amari Rise Publishing
3314 San Felipe Road #917 San Jose, CA 95134

The publisher acknowledges the co-authors who graciously granted our team permission to reprint the enclosed material.

Each author is writing from her own experience and viewpoint and does not necessarily reflect the viewpoint or thought of the reader. The contents of this book, such as text and references, are for informational purposes only. The content is not intended to be a substitute for professional advice and expertise concerning mental health diagnosis or psychiatric treatment. Always seek out and adhere to the advice of your mental health professional or qualified health provider. Never disregard professional advice or delay in seeking it because of something you have read in this book.

The authors, clinical consultant, and publisher made every attempt and effort to ensure that the information in this book was correct at the time of press. We do not assume and hereby disclaim any liability to any party, including the reader, for any loss, damage, or disruption caused by errors or omissions, whether such errors or omissions result from negligence, accident, or any other cause. The reader, or any party, cannot hold the authors, clinical consultant, and publisher or any other members of the team accountable for any outcomes or conclusions that come as a result of reading this book.

Dedication

I dedicate this book to Richard and Davonte, my two essential "why-factors." You two have helped fuel the passion in my life, and in my most critical times, you reminded me why I could not quit! To the best collaborating team (Dr. Nat, Valerie, Darlena, Donna, Billie, and Lameisha), who have "burned the midnight oil" to make this book happen, thank you! To the Honorable, Lady of Grace, Bishop Ernestine Cleveland Reems, whose trail-blazing spirit and coaching motivated the team "to get it done," thank you! To every endorser who believed in this project, your words will make an indelible impression on the readers, thank you! To my parents, Bishop Emeritus John Erwin, Sr. and Mrs. Norma Erwin, thank you, for being the lighted guideposts of wisdom for the team and this project. To all the family members, friends, and village-partners journeying with a loved one with a mental health diagnosis, you are truly key assets on the journey. To those loved ones with a psychological diagnosis, we honor you! May you experience a level of hope as you read every page of this book. To those loved ones who have passed on, we cherish your memory. To every person who has purchased this book as a resource, thank you! May the first-person accounts reflected in this literary work serve as a catalyst toward change. Last but not least, to the Supreme Author, thank you for entrusting the team and I with this mission!

Teresa A. Tate

Table of Contents

Foreword... xiii

Preface: A Word from Our Author......................... xvii

1 Surviving Suicide: A Grandmother's
Story of Love and Loss
By Billie Davis 21

2 Identifying the Family Effects: How Mental
Illness Impacts The Family Unit
By Reverend Donna Edward 33

3 Pushing Past the Pain: A Family's Journey
Through Stigma and Grief
By Darlena Mays..47

4 Stepping Up to the Plate: Choosing to Support Loved Ones
with Mental Illness
By Valerie Watson-Smith...53

5 Navigating Rocky Terrain: Tough Decisions Encountered
When Supporting Loved Ones with Mental Illness
By Teresa A. Tate & Valerie Watson-Smith.................59

6 Confronting Stigma: When Mental Illness
Comes to Your Door
By Teresa A. Tate & Dr. Natalie Watson-Singleton 73

7 Letting Go Of Anger: Making Peace
with the Broken Pieces
By Teresa A. Tate 81

8 Embracing the New Normal: Setting Realistic
Expectations for Life with a Loved One with Mental Illness
By Teresa A. Tate 87

Concluding Thoughts: A Word from Our Author &
Clinical Consultant 95

About the Author...97

About the Collaborators 99

About the Clinical Consultant 103

Resource List..105

References 109

Foreword

As an esteemed Bishop with over 75 years in the ministry, I have come to appreciate the lessons and blessings of my journey. When God called me to pastor, church leadership was male dominated, making me a trailblazer for other women to serve God in the same capacity. During my ministry journey, I was blessed to have founded the Kingdom Builders Ministerial Alliance and Center of Hope Community Church. I also purchased a 150-unit affordable housing complex, a 56-unit apartment building for seniors, and a 17-unit transitional facility for homeless single women with children in Oakland, California.

Throughout the years, God has blessed me to mentor many men and women both nationally and internationally. I have numerous spiritual daughters, and one of those special gems is Teresa A. Tate. She is a humble servant and a caring mother who is comfortable sharing how her son's mental health diagnosis affected her and her family. Because of these experiences, she has a passion to help others understand mental illness, to inform others of the resources available when supporting a loved one with a mental health diagnosis, and to assist families and friends with the healing process. This God-given project is written in such a way that the reader can actually visualize the healing steps, feel the pain of mental illness, and enjoy the results of recovery.

God has given her a mandate to be an *Advocate* and a *Voice* with a clear message concerning the plight of those who live with the challenges that stem from having a psychological health concern. During my many years as a bishop, I have witnessed people sweep mental illness under the rug. Unfortunately, the topic of mental illness has received minimal attention from the church, workforce, and communities, and many families have ignored this "elephant in the room." Yet, in order to truly heal and to meet the needs of those with mental health concerns, it is critical to be honest and to recognize the signs of mental illness.

Teresa A. Tate challenges the reader to:

- Resist secrecy
- Resist the urge to ignore the signs of mental illness
- Resist the temptation to make every situation a spiritual battle rather than an actual health concern
- Resist overlooking multiple and varied resources that God places in our path

By helping the reader to understand the different aspects of mental health diagnoses, treatment, and recovery, this unique book project tackles the highs and lows of the decision-making process and the difficult emotions that occur along the way when caring for loved ones with mental illness. A distinct strength of this book is its collaborative approach. The compilation of stories and perspectives from different writers allows the reader to see how mental illness does not just affect the individual living with the diagnosis, but it also impacts the whole family. As you read this text, you will hear the voices of different family members – mothers, grandmothers, and aunts – and how they collaborated with professionals, mental health facilities, and their loved one to ensure their loved one's health and wellness. Even when things did not go as desired, as in the case of a loved one's suicide, the writers effectively use their words and stories to paint a transparent picture.

You will be able to enter their world and see their perspectives and experience the reactions of their family members. You will feel empowered to make decisions and to identify the signs of emerging crises or relapse. You will learn what steps to take and how to move within the appropriate timing. This book will help you combat fear, stigma, and shame so that you can apply the information and resources while accepting the support of your family and community.

In conclusion, I have observed Teresa walk through this tumultuous road and turn her challenges into ministry for hurting people. Her journey has planted the seeds for this collaborative book project so that each and every reader can recognize the signs of mental illness and know how to facilitate the healing process. Know that you are not alone, *"For God hath not given us the Spirit of fear; but of power, and of love, and of a sound mind"* 2 Timothy 1:7 – Be assured that the God who is all-knowing sees your hurts and struggles and wants to care for you and your loved ones, and He has commissioned this collaborative book project so that you do not have to stay in pain and suffer in silence. Today, seek support, resist shame, and allow the healing of hope to take place.

Bishop Ernestine Cleveland Reems
Oakland, California

Preface:
A Word from Our Author

I will never forget the day in 2009 when I received a call from my sister. She was very concerned about my youngest son, and she wanted to ask him if he would spend a few days with her and my parents at their home. I could detect the sense of urgency in her voice. I consented, and she called him that same night. From the time my son arrived at their home, my life has never been the same. The life I had previously known and experienced with my son had drastically changed.

Prior to the day my sister called me, I remember noticing subtle changes in my son's behavior; these behaviors became more erratic and unpredictable over time. I first noticed he had difficulty processing information and following basic instructions. When I inquired about his hobbies or asked about his day, he appeared to have lost interest in things he used to enjoy, and he had difficulty expressing himself. The face that once contained an effervescent smile that could light up any room become stone-faced and flat. Even his well-groomed trend-setting ways had given way to a disheveled appearance. Our playful interactions were replaced by his social detachment and withdrawal; he began distancing himself from family, and it appeared as if he preferred to be alone. Then, there were days he dreaded being alone and would show up unannounced at the house of two of my dear friends (Thank You J & K!). Despite these changes, I assumed they were just what "teenage boys go through." However, all in all, although some of these changes were indicative of normal adolescence, others were the emerging signs of mental illness.

The Mayo Clinic defines mental illness as "a wide range of mental health conditions — disorders that affect mood, thinking, and behavior."[1] Mental illness can include an array of disorders, like depression, bipolar, anxiety, schizophrenia, and addictive behaviors, all of which come with their own set of symptoms and causes. Unfortunately, most of the experiences I have described are far too common.

According to the National Alliance of Mental Illness (NAMI), 1 in 4 adults have experienced mental health symptoms at least once during their lifetime.[2] This means that over 40 million Americans – more than the populations of New York and Florida combined – are living with or have lived with symptoms of mental illness.[3] These rates are even more concerning for youth. Youth mental illness rates are on the rise, such that youth depression has increased from 8.5% in 2011 to 11.1% in 2014. Despite these steady increases, approximately 80% of youth are left with no or insufficient mental health treatment.[4]

Throughout this journey, I have learned that psychological concerns transcend credentials, race, gender, socioeconomic status, and religious affiliation. It does not care if you are a CEO, doctor, pastor, plumber, or daycare worker. I am a mother, daughter, sister, community leader, and published author, and every day I must make the decision to fulfill my multiple roles while caring for my son. This is why I felt compelled and inspired to share my story and journey with others through this book.

Caring for a loved one with a mental health diagnosis is a difficult task. Depending on the diagnosis and where an individual is in his/her process, family members can find themselves having to make tough decisions all while managing the stigmas and the various emotions that come with having a loved one with a mental health condition. This is why I was inspired to put together this collaborative book project, *Coming Out of Darkness: A Family's Journey Through Mental Illness*. This book highlights the experiences and accounts of family members – mothers, grandmothers, and aunts– who make a decision to "show up and be present" while living through the highs and lows of having a loved one with a diagnosis. In this book, you will read about different authors' life experiences, personal observations, and clinical knowledge regarding how to come out of the darkness of shame, misinformation, and self-blame to effectively support your loved one and to navigate mental health treatment options.

In addition to providing first person accounts of having a loved one with a mental health diagnosis, this book aims to (a) offer hope to families experiencing the effects of watching a loved one battle mental illness, (b) provide suggestions on how to support loved ones throughout their journey to mental health wellness, (c) raise awareness about mental illness, and (d) challenge misperceptions about mental illness in society. I hope this book brings comfort, knowledge, and clarity to best assist you in your process of supporting your loved one.

A Mother Who Loves Her Son,

Teresa A. Tate

1

Surviving Suicide: A Grandmother's Story of Love and Loss
By Billie Davis

My grandson was intelligent, witty, smart, outgoing, and a world traveler. At the age 4, he was extremely computer savvy – teaching me how to navigate the computer and internet when everyone else gave up. By the age of 12, he was trying to figure out ways to earn his own income. He started selling my old jewelry on eBay before I even knew what eBay was. In my opinion, he was a genius.

By the time he was in high school, he desired to be a holistic medicine physician. He went on to college, and studied herbal medicine. Through his studies, our family learned about holistic healing compared to traditional medicine.

My vibrant, humorous, and gregarious grandson transformed before my very eyes. He was seventeen when he was officially diagnosed with depression. I started to notice the signs when he lived with me back in 2009. He was sleeping a lot, alienating the family, and experiencing serious mood swings. It progressed to the point where his mother and I agreed to take him to see a psychologist. I remember taking him to his first session. I waited in the waiting room because I wanted him to have his privacy and to feel comfortable speaking on any topics without me in the room. After his first meeting, the psychologist informed me that my grandson was displaying symptoms of depression. Because he met criteria for clinical depression and because of the severity of his symptoms, he was prescribed medication. He started taking the medication immediately. He was eager to look up the medications, and he thoroughly researched their side effects. He appeared to be truly invested in this process, and he was excited for his follow-up appointment with the psychologist two weeks later. After about two weeks (which is the usual amount of time it takes for psychiatric medication to kick in), my grandson reported he was feeling better. I even noticed changes, which indicated that he was, in fact, improving. It appeared as if everything was taking a turn for the better.

Unfortunately, these changes were short lived. A couple of months later he lapsed back into his old routine; he was sleeping all day, missing school, isolating himself from family, and exhibiting anger and violent behaviors. He had stopped taking the medication. However, his use of marijuana increased. I had suspicions that he used marijuana recreationally, but it had now intensified to the point where he felt he needed it to relax. According to him, the other medications made him feel "funny," which is something I have heard so many others say. I do believe many people discontinue their medications because they do not like how they feel when they are on them. However, his decision to discontinue the medications only exacerbated his already difficult symptoms.

In the summer of 2013, my grandson gave his life to Christ. He was baptized at a church not far from his home. He started singing in the choir, going to Sunday services, and attending bible study regularly; he was determined to get closer to God. As a woman of faith, I was overjoyed by this. I was convinced that this would be a new beginning for he and his family; this was going to be the missing link that would finally turn his life around. Although I was often traveling due to work, he and I talked every day. We prayed together and read scriptures together. My hope in his recovery had returned, and I was rejuvenated by the possibilities of what his life could now become. Yet, even this was not enough to prevent the worse from happening.

In the winter of 2013, he experienced several hospital admissions, most of which lasted about two to three days. The hospital stays were just enough to calm him down with injections, and he was always sent home to manage his mental illness with the help of family. Interestingly, although I am a registered nurse, even I was not equipped for what would occur during the next year. He began to hear voices, and his violent behavior escalated to the point we thought he may hurt family members. Because of this, his mother helped him settle into his own apartment. This newfound independence actually seemed like it was going to be a positive thing. For the first time in a long time, he appeared motivated to get his own job, which he was able to maintain for a little while. However, this did not last. He ended up in the hospital for the fourth time, at which point he was finally diagnosed with schizophrenia. He remained in the hospital for fourteen days so the doctors could adequately stabilize him. Yet, when he was released, he exploded and damaged the car during an altercation with his mom as they were leaving the hospital. This led me to believe that the doctors actually discharged him prematurely. Ultimately, he had to be re-hospitalized that same night for an additional seven days.

After his release that time, he went to live with his father. Although my daughter and I were grateful for the additional family support, his father did not believe in mental illness. Rather, his dad believed he was simply acting like a bad, unruly, and disrespectful child. This only fueled the problematic behaviors as well as caused my grandson to feel unheard, misunderstood, and alone. After about two months, his father eventually kicked him out of the house. My grandson ended up on the streets. He was taken to the hospital again after being found wandering around the woods without clothes. Again, we were back to the same pattern - in and out of the hospital. In between hospital stays, he also was arrested several times for vagrancy. He spent time in the county jail, and he later shared he had been raped by an officer while there. Although we never found any proof, I believed it happened just as he said. Unfortunately, people with mental health diagnoses are often targets of abuse, misuse, and violence, and they are often taken advantage of in these institutions because they can be discredited as "crazy." When he was not in the hospital or in jail, he was living on the street or in shelters.

By January 2014, he had really declined. He lost weight, and he ignored his grooming and hygiene. However, he and I still talked daily on the phone, and on several occasions I would pick him up and bring him home with me so he could spend time with the family. Although we enjoyed seeing him and spending time with him, the schizophrenia was often too much for us all to handle. There were many times we did not know what to do or say or how to interact with him. We loved him, but we often felt at a loss with how to best navigate his mental health symptoms.

Eventually his mom found him a group home to stay in. The group home worked out pretty well for a while, but it did not prevent him from ending up in the hospital again. When he ended up in the hospital, I went to see him while he was there, and we talked about God and scriptures. We spent time laughing about past family events and memories. He said the new medicine was working, and the voices were not as frequent. It was also during this time that he revealed to me his HIV diagnosis, which he received in 2012. Interestingly, he told me that he could live with the HIV, but it was enormously difficult to live with the voices.

He also shared that he was concerned that if he continued his psychiatric medication, the side effects would slow down his immune system and increase his chances of developing AIDS. I encouraged him to trust God and to know that God had a plan for him. Our visit ended with him telling me he felt closer to God than he had ever felt before. We hugged, and he gave me a big kiss. He told me not to worry because God was with him. This visit was on Saturday, May 3rd.

On the morning of May 5th, as I was getting ready to fly out for work, I stopped by the hospital to drop off new clothes and shoes. I also gave him $40 for pocket change. I arrived at my destination at 11:00 am, and I immediately called him to make sure his day was going well. He sounded great, and he was excited about his new clothes and sneakers. He also was looking forward to going back to the group home once he was discharged. I felt good when I heard this as it seemed like it had been so long since he had felt excited and hopeful. Never did I assume that at 3:00pm I would receive the worst call a parent or grandparent could receive. My grandson had hanged himself.*

Our entire family was devastated by my grandson's suicide. Even now, there are days when the pain feels like it will consume everything in its wake. No one could have prepared me for that call. When I first heard the news, I was numb. When the numbness started to clear, I started to question how this happened and what we could have done to prevent it. I think the feeling was

---

*Although the term "commit suicide" is widely used when referring to suicide, the suicide prevention community has rejected this term. When the verb "commit" is followed by an action or behavior, it typically represents a sinful or immoral action (e.g., commit murder, commit adultery). Thus, this language invokes judgement and further stigmatizes individuals who experience suicidal ideation and/or who die by suicide. The recommended terms are "killed him/herself," "took his/her own life," and "died by suicide."

worse because he did not leave a letter, so we were left wondering why he killed himself. In addition, as I watched my daughter hurting, I wanted to help her, but I also needed help. We did our best to support each other during this difficult time, but our support for each other was limited by our own pain and suffering.

Although I have given this situation over to God, I still experience immense sadness because of his absence. I miss my grandson so much that even this chapter was written with tears streaming down my face. Even today, I continue to struggle with the lack of closure regarding his death. I still question if there was more I should have done. Occasionally, tears fill my eyes as I think about the experiences I will never have with my grandson – I will never see him get married, create and sustain his own business, and grow old alongside my other grandchildren. Because of this, there were moments I did not think I would be able to finish these pages because the sadness was too intense. Yet, I pressed through hoping to lend support, comfort, and direction to others who are doing their best to support their loved ones with mental illness. Although I would never wish this experience on anyone, I have been able to make space for the lessons I have learned from his death. What follows are some suggestions on the warning signs and prevention strategies for suicide that I have learned from my own personal experience.

Know the warning signs

Suicide is one of the leading causes of death across the world. There is no single trigger for a suicide attempt, but it most often happens when stressors and health issues interact to produce feelings of hopelessness and despair.

Suicide can affect anyone, yet, certain groups are at an increased risk for suicide. It is important to note that not everyone with a mental illness is likely to die by suicide. Data from the American Foundation for Suicide Prevention indicates that people who are at an elevated risk are people with severe depression, bipolar disorder, schizophrenia, substance use disorders, impulse control disorders, personality disorders, and significant physical health conditions (e.g., chronic pain). Because of this, it is important to know your loved one's diagnosis given that this can help you appropriately assess risk.

Families can play an important role in preventing suicide. According to the American Foundation for Suicide Prevention, there are common changes in speech, behaviors, and mood that can signal that your loved one may be thinking about suicide.

Changes in speech can include talking more about:
- Killing themselves
- Feeling hopeless
- Having no reason to live
- Being a burden to others
- Feeling trapped
- Unbearable pain

Changes in behavior can include:
- Increased alcohol or drugs use
- Looking for ways to end their lives (e.g., researching methods online)
- Withdrawing from activities
- Isolating from family and friends
- Sleeping too much or too little
- Visiting or calling people to say goodbye
- Giving away prized possessions
- Aggression

Changes in mood can include:
- Depression
- Anxiety
- Loss of interest
- Irritability
- Humiliation/Shame
- Agitation/Anger
- Relief/Sudden Improvement

If you notice these warning signs and think your loved one may be thinking about suicide, it is important for you to initiate the conversation rather than wait for them to reach out to you. Here are some strategies from the American Foundation for Suicide Prevention on how to talk to your loved one:

- Talk to them in private
- Listen to their story – do not interrupt or debate the value of life. Do not minimize their problems or give advice
- Tell them you care about them
- Ask directly if they are thinking about suicide (e.g., "Are you thinking about hurting yourself?")
- Encourage them to seek treatment or to contact their doctor or therapist

If your loved one shares that he or she is thinking about suicide, here is what you can do:

- Take them seriously
- Stay with them
- Help them remove lethal means (e.g., guns, knives, pills, ropes, plastic bags)

- Call the *National Suicide Prevention Lifeline* at *1-800-273-8255*
- Text TALK to *741741* to text with a trained crisis counselor from the *Crisis Text Line* for free, 24/7
- Escort them to mental health services or an emergency room

Listen to your gut feeling

Looking back, I sometimes wonder if things would have been different had I informed the doctor of some of my grandson's behaviors early on. Now that I truly look back on his behaviors, I do believe his schizophrenia symptoms could have been diagnosed earlier. Which eventually was the disease that cost him his life.

Also, if you suspect that your loved one is suicidal, ask. Many people believe that asking someone if they are suicidal will trigger them to end their life. This is not the case. Although your loved one may become upset with you for asking if he or she is suicidal, for many people it creates an invitation to talk about something they are struggling to make sense of. Asking them also can be a signal that you are up for the task of helping them stay safe. If your loved one denies being suicidal, and you suspect he or she is not being honest, still go with your gut feeling by letting your loved one know you are there to talk about it when he or she is ready.

Looking back on the situation with my grandson, one thing I would have done differently is tracked changes in his behaviors, moods, and thoughts when they occurred. By writing down these changes, I would have been prepared to share these changes with doctors. This would have prevented me from waiting until we were in crisis to recreate how things were going. A regular log of changes and events is helpful because it serves as an objective measure of the type and frequency of changes you are witnessing. Also, when you know something is wrong or different with your loved one, it is much easier for a doctor to understand your concerns and offer assistance when you provide specific data.

Seek Support

As I stated previously, despite our unconditional love for my grandson, my family and I were unsure how to best support him. We enjoyed having him at family gatherings, yet when he was around and experiencing active psychotic symptoms, we often did not know how to "be" with him. I think this placed added stress on the family as well as on my grandson. Looking back, I wish my family and I would have sought out specific resources for families who had loved ones with psychological conditions. Simply learning how to interact with him in ways that were sensitive to his illness and respectful of his personhood and dignity may have allowed for less stress on both sides. I cannot know for sure if this would have prevented his suicide, but it is something I would encourage other families to try.

Recognize the opportunities and challenges of psychiatric hospitalizations

My grandson was repeatedly in and out of the hospital because of his mental health symptoms. What I have since learned is that this is common, especially for people with severe mental illness (e.g., schizophrenia). Although my family and I thought these hospitalizations were supposed to help and rehabilitate my grandson, this was not the case. There have been significant changes to hospitalizations in general and psychiatric admissions specifically. Specifically, there used to be a time when long-term mental health care was the norm. However, in the 1960s and 1970s, funding for long-term care was replaced with funding for community mental health centers. The idea was that by encouraging people to seek support from mental health centers in the community rather than from long-term asylums would help them better re-integrate back into society. However, this resulted in fewer resources for long-term care; by 2010, there were only 43,000 psychiatric beds available, which equates to only about 14 beds per 100,000 people.[5] Because there is not enough room in these facilities to serve people with severe mental illness, they are more likely to end up homeless, in jail, or in prison.

Because my family and I were not fully aware of these dynamics at the time, I believe we had unrealistic expectations for the hospital. We expected the hospital to help him get better and to only release him if he was better. Yet, this was not the case. The hospital only stabilized him enough for him to receive outpatient care services. Therefore, his symptoms and old behaviors had not been cured; rather they had only been temporarily subdued. Although we wanted to believe he was better after his discharge, these lulls of symptoms were always short lived. This would leave my family and I feeling as if the hospital only treated him until they needed his bed for someone else.

If you have had a similar experience where you felt your loved one was discharged too soon, you are not alone. I felt that my grandson's hospital care was rushed, and I have come to learn that many families with loved ones with severe mental illness feel this way. One tip for families would be to advocate for a clear and thorough discharge plan. Demand that hospital staff do not release your loved one until they have made sure that he or she is capable of taking his or her medication. Make sure that staff have provided proper housing referrals so that your loved one can move into an appropriate and stable living situation. Also, request referrals for outpatient services. These are services, like individual therapy, medication management, and day programs. These outpatient services are essential in ensuring that your loved one can truly learn new skills to manage their mental health symptoms and prevent relapse.

~

Mental illness can have devastating effects on any family. Various responsibilities come with supporting loved ones with psychological health concerns. To ensure the overall wellness and functioning of the family unit, families need to know the resources and contacts that exist in their communities and to know the signs and symptoms of their loved one's illness.

2

Identifying the Family Effects:
How Mental Illness Impacts
The Family Unit
By Reverend Donna Edward

Let me first start with my "Revy D" disclaimer. Contained in these few pages are scenarios that reflect my perspective, vantage point, and observations of real time experiences interacting with loved ones with mental illness.

I have been a licensed and ordained minister for the past 20 years, and more recently, I have become a certified professional life coach. In these roles, I have had the privilege to walk up-close and personal with families of all socioeconomic levels and ethnic backgrounds to search for answers on how to support and love their family member(s) dealing with mental health challenges. In addition, for several years I have had the privilege to work for the largest private non-profit mental health agency in California's Santa Clara County as a corporate recruiter hiring over 450 full time psychiatrists and professional clinical staff to meet the high demands of our ever-growing client population.

Throughout my experiences, I have observed that having a loved one with mental illness† has ripple effects for the entire family unit. Whether the family consists of parents and their children or grandparents and their grandchildren, the family unit is unique, diverse, and a powerful entity. When something, like mental illness, affects one member of the family, it affects the entire entity. Although the impact can vary in terms of degree based on an array of factors, the truth remains that mental illness comes with many family effects that must be recognized, acknowledged, and worked through.

Before I delve into these family effects, I first want to say that if you are facing the realities of having a loved one with a psychological concern, please know these three things:

You are Not Alone
Judgement Stops Now
You are Shame and Guilt FREE!

Although there are various family effects that emerge when you have a loved one with a mental health diagnosis, in my experience working with families, the effects that have been most pronounced are denial, the blame game, bitterness, isolation, financial burdens, and burnout.

---

†The phrase, "loved one with mental illness" reflects "person first language." According to the American Psychological Association, person first language honors individuals as people first rather than reduce them to their disability. When we use terms that do not reflect person first language, like "a schizophrenic person" (rather than "a person with schizophrenia") we emphasize the disability over the person's humanity, which can perpetuate stereotypes.

Denial

Denial haunts many families who have a loved one with a psychological condition. In psychological terms, denial refers to a defense mechanism – or coping strategy – that occurs when a person (or family) rejects the truth of a situation or disregards facts that are too devastating or uncomfortable to accept.[6] The situation and facts are overlooked as untrue even in the midst of overwhelming evidence. The purpose of denial is to protect; I have seen families operate in denial to protect the family's image, emotional well-being, or cohesion. For instance, depending on your relationship with the family member with mental illness, you may struggle with feelings of jealousy because perhaps that family member requires more time and attention from others. Often, if a sibling has a mental health diagnosis, the other sibling may feel neglected or pressured to overcompensate for the sibling with the illness. These feelings and emotions can be difficult to process, and they are suppressed and denied to manage daily life.

Some family members may find themselves living in the land of denial because they are afraid of what would happen if they faced their real emotions. For example, because mental health challenges come with various "unknowns," it is possible for family members to feel angry and resentful towards their family member who has a mental illness because they view them as inconveniencing and disrupting an already busy and demanding life. Facing the fact that you may feel jealous, angry, or resentful toward your loved one with mental illness may lead to secondary feelings of shame and guilt. Therefore, families become stuck in the habit of shutting off these emotions through the numbing allure of denial. However, what families soon discover is that denial is not an effective strategy for moving closer to healing and recovery.

Denial can manifest differently across families, and for some it can manifest as beliefs that the illness will "pass" or just be a "phase." For other families, the denial manifests as inaccurate explanations for the behavior, like "that's just how he/she is" or "my loved one is just lazy or unruly." Unfortunately, adopting these beliefs hides the truth of the matter and blocks families from unlocking helpful tactics. Families then find themselves stuck in old patterns year after year. Unfortunately, remaining in a place of denial can result in estranged familial relationships, family breakdown, and division.

In my experience working with families, I have found that denial is most pronounced in "picture-perfect families" – these are the families characterized by great parents, great support systems, educated family members, and maybe even active community members and church-goers. These are the families where there appears to be no rhyme or reason for why a loved one has developed mental illness. Because we often presume that mental illness only affects certain kinds of people, we are shocked when it shows up in our homes, families, and communities. Yet, mental illness does not care who you are, and anyone can find him/herself a part of the growing statistic of 1 in 4 Americans living with mental illness.[7] The first step to coming out from under the cloak of denial is to confront and accept the reality of mental illness. If you are unsure if the signs and symptoms displayed by your family member are consistent with a mental health condition, I encourage you to seek counsel from a medical and/or mental health professional. Once you know what you are up against, you can confront it with acceptance, knowledge, and wisdom.

The Blame Game

When mental illness is introduced into our lives, we can feel confused and as if we have lost control. The life that was once contained and orderly, starts to feel uncontrollable and in disarray. It can be difficult to believe our life as we knew it, lived it, loved it has drastically changed. Because of this, a common tactic is to slip into the blame-game. Whether we blame others, our loved ones, or ourselves, blame helps us provide an explanation for something that is inherently inexplicable.

Blame refers to our tendency to assign fault or responsibility for some event or occurrence,[8] and it can function to lessen our uncertainty and to enhance our perceptions of control. For instance, it can be challenging to grapple with the uncertainties and unknowns of mental illness. Therefore, we find ourselves asking, "Why me? Why my family? Why now?" Then, we may find ourselves producing answers, like "My parents caused my brother's depression by being too hard on him." Unfortunately, these answers obscure the complex reality of mental illness. This does not mean that mental illness just comes out of the blue. No, there are real factors, like genetics, family environments, and poverty, which contribute to the presence of mental illness. I also believe God can provide divine insight into the roots of your particular family situation. However, do not become too caught up in blaming or trying to explain the "why" that you forget the power of having faith during difficult times.

Bitterness

If you are not careful, bitterness can become a part of your life's existence. It is imperative that we make the conscious decision to not become bitter. Please do whatever it takes to determine NO MATTER WHAT, I refuse to become bitter. Personally, I protect myself from bitterness by adopting this daily confession: "My flesh and my heart may fail, but God is the strength of my heart and my portion forever." (Ps. 73.26)

Bitterness may be hard to admit, but it is often easy to recognize. It is like a beach ball that we try to submerge in the water; yet, no matter how valiant our efforts, it pops up with all of its vitality. Bitterness can be one of the most dangerous and destructive human emotions if we do not properly deal with it. By definition, bitterness is a feeling of hurt, resentment, anger, and hate that has built up through unforgiveness or our inability to let go of hurt inflicted by another person or life experience. [9] I also believe we become bitter as a result of feeling as if we have lost control over some aspect of our life. When someone close to us experiences mental health challenges, we often feel out of control. We may become bitter and resentful toward them for not taking their medication as prescribed, not consistently working their treatment plan, or experiencing relapse. For some, the bitterness may come from feeling as if the family reputation is negatively impacted or as if the family's "good name" is tarnished. Whatever the reasons, we start to notice bitterness corroding our dreams and eating away at our joy, faith, and contentment.

I really want to encourage you – you are not alone. You are not hopeless or helpless. You and God are in control and there are always options and alternatives! You can let go of bitterness, and you and your loved one can enjoy a meaningful relationship and valuable connectedness with each other and be committed to each other's success. One way to let go of bitterness is to be clear about what you can control and what you cannot control. Although you may not be able to control if your loved one relapses, you can control how you show up for them and support them through the process. The parts that you cannot control, release them, and determine that love, humility and prayer will be a part of your daily routine. Keep love as your focus. Love never fails! Love is so powerful that it can cover every feeling of blame, hurt, shame, resentment and bitterness. Choose love!

Isolation

It is easy to feel isolated and helpless when you are supporting a loved one with a mental health diagnosis. You may find yourself wondering, "Who do I run to?" "Where is my safe place to fall?"

Research has shown that families of persons dealing with mental illness can experience stigma because of having a loved one with a diagnosis. Unfortunately, this stigma can result in blame, social isolation, and rejection.

Stigma can lead to the "community" silently isolating the family by making them uncomfortable when they bring their loved one with mental illness to social events. It is sad to say, but I have actually witnessed this happen. A family had a loved one with schizophrenia, and the person with schizophrenia would sometimes become agitated, which resulted in him pacing and speaking in an elevated tone. Although he never became violent or threatened anyone's safety, other people were uncomfortable with his presence. Therefore, when others in the community planned parties for different events (e.g. holiday season), they would find a million excuses to not invite this family for fear that they would bring their loved one. These community members felt they had to make certain choices based on "fear and stigma" and not based on facts and real life experiences.

39

Families can also experience isolation for a variety of reasons, including "blaming and shaming." Because of people's lack of knowledge about the causes of mental illness, many people blame the family unit for their loved one's behavior. This in turn can cause families to withdraw and isolate from their social circles.

If you find yourself feeling alone in your experience of assisting your loved one with mental illness, here are several things you can do:[10]

First, speak up. Please do not hurt alone! You may find what you need by speaking to someone who is having similar experiences. Also, tell friends and family members how they can support you; a common misperception is that people should automatically know what you need. However, this is not true, and I encourage you to be up front about what is going on with you. If you are unsure about what you need, take time to self-reflect and then write down your needs. Once your needs are written down, it will be easier to identify people who can help and provide assistance. This also allows you to involve as many family and friends as possible. For instance, some people may be able to provide dinner twice a month whereas others may be happy to call different community agencies to pinpoint transitional housing options, support groups, or additional resources. Moreover, do not be limited to those who live in your same city. Even family members who live far away may be able to provide assistance from a distance.

Second, set up regular check-ins with a designated family member or friend. This person can call you on a set basis (e.g., weekly) in order to check in to receive status updates and/or requests. This point person can then help you spread this information to others in your community circle. For instance, if you need assistance grocery shopping that week, this person can help you call around and identify those who can step in and assist with this task. This will save you the time and emotional energy from having to update each family member and friend with what is going on, which can be taxing in its own right.

Third, when someone offers to help, say "yes." For some of us, we ask God for help, but then when help arrives, we act too shy, proud, or controlling to accept it. This is another reason why it can be good to have a list of your needs; it allows you to easily communicate with others about how they can help. Also, by saying yes, you are giving others the opportunity to feel good about supporting you.

Overall, I have witnessed better outcomes when families unify and focus on their loved one's recovery and restoration. I do know that when we rally together, there is strength in numbers. Feel free to engage your other family members to make joint decisions concerning your loved one. Encourage others within the family unit to make a "love choice" to support your family member. It may not be "equal giving" but hopefully "equal sacrifice." It is true, in a multitude of counsel, there is safety.

Choose not to isolate for fear of being mocked or ridiculed because of "association." Although society and small communities can try to inflict it, the simplest ingredients of family and community will assist in the promotion of recovery.

Financial Burdens

Even your finances can change considerably when you are actively supporting a loved one with mental illness. It can be overwhelming and challenging to have to care not only physically and emotionally for someone, but also to be responsible for his or her daily living expenses. Psychological research has revealed that among family members who have loved ones with mental health conditions, financial constraints were a concern.[11] For some family members, there is limited time to work and earn money because of time spent caring for relatives. In some situations, family members have to take leaves of absence from their jobs. In my experience, I have noticed that it is especially difficult for individuals who have a spouse with mental health challenges. Depending on the spouse's diagnosis, he or she may have times in his/her life where he/she is not earning regularly due to illness. Because of this, the other spouse may temporarily become the only wage-earning member of the family, further straining the family's financial situation.

Additionally, family members may have to cover their loved one's costs. If the loved one is unable to work due to his/her mental health diagnosis or if his/her governmental assistance is insufficient, family members may be called upon to cover rent, car note/insurance, weekly allowance, utilities, medications, and other activities for their loved one. After a period of time, you may even become their "conservator," in which you become responsible for your loved one's financial affairs and/or daily life.

Unfortunately, research reveals that most people are not financially prepared for the role of caregiving.[12] Especially if the needed care is prolonged. With 1 in 4 people most likely to experience a mental health condition during their lifetime, it is vital to explore all the possible resources available to prevent severe financial harm and impact. One vital strategy is to reach out to professional resources and referrals. Resources will vary from state to state, and city to city, yet, in several regions, there are governmental and federal resources to support people living with mental illness.

It can be difficult, but it is very important to set real boundaries and expectations concerning how much financial support families are willing and able to contribute. One helpful strategy may include meeting with a financial advisor who can walk families through the benefits and drawbacks of different options, like co-signing, shared credit for leases, loans, and credit cards. Setting financial boundaries can help protect families from additional strain and prevent feelings of bitterness and resentment that can arise when people feel emotionally, physically, and financially strapped.

Burnout

Juggling the responsibilities that come with having a loved one with a mental health diagnosis can be grueling. Depending on the responsibilities associated with supporting your loved one, you may find yourself traveling long distances to visit your loved one in a hospital setting, scheduling appointments within inconvenient visiting hours, and spending time in uncomfortable and sterile facilities. Not to mention, your emotions can be all over the place, but you still have to maintain a nurturing posture. You may also find yourself doing all that you can for your loved one only to discover he/she is not in a place to receive your help or assistance. This can leave you feeling rejected and helpless.

Sometimes the pressure can feel overwhelming, especially if you are doing it alone or if you did not anticipate being the primary caregiver. More often than not, the pressure to provide support, answers, and resources can take its toll. If you continue to support your loved one without taking time to rest, refresh, and rejuvenate, the stress can compromise your health, relationships, and state of mind—eventually leading to burnout.[13] In fact, research has demonstrated that family caregivers experience elevated rates of poor health, like high blood pressure/hypertension, arthritis, high cholesterol, obesity, and diabetes, which may be due to the stress of caring for chronically ill family members.[14] I am reminded of Eleanor Brownn's quote, "Rest and self-care are so important. You cannot serve from an empty vessel." This quote highlights how taking care of yourself "isn't a luxury—it's a necessity."

Burnout can manifest in various ways. Here are some common signs that indicate that you may be experiencing caregiver burnout and stress:[15]

- Having much less energy than you once had
- Neglecting your own needs and responsibilities, either because you're too busy or you don't care anymore
- Feeling increasingly resentful
- Drinking, smoking, or eating more
- Cutting back on leisure activities
- Overreacting to minor nuisances
- Difficulty sleeping

The first step to overcoming burnout is realizing that it is ok not to have it all together all the time. To support your loved one, you do not have to do anything beyond what you feel you are able to do. Sometimes you may have to give yourself the gift of a temporary weekend get-a-way, especially if you are responsible for caretaking. You may have to give yourself the gift of a few short hours alone to self-reflect and enjoy self-care. Daily devotions and spirit-filled worship are great tools for rejuvenation.

~

On this healing journey, the quest is to be open, transparent, honest, and deliberate with the goal of bringing about full health and wellness to your loved one as well as to every family member impacted by the illness. What I hope for is compassion, not only for the person suffering, but also for those who accompany the sufferer. Wherever you find yourself on this journey, please be encouraged and know that, although mental disorders are serious, they are very treatable. Though you may not have the power to change your circumstances or erase away your loved one's diagnosis, you do have the power and grace to determine how you will respond and react to it.

If I could encourage someone who feels overwhelmed by these circumstances, I would say, please reach out, please use this reading as a handy tool, and please research additional resources that can bring strength and hope. It is my sincere prayer that you stay the course and enjoy a much-fulfilled family life overflowing with peace and hope. Perhaps you want to agree with me in prayer:

Dear Heavenly Father, I come to you in the precious name of Jesus Christ, and I thank you that because of Calvary, you bore ALL of our sickness and disease. You were wounded for our transgressions, bruised for our iniquities, the chastisement of our peace was upon you and by your stripes we are healed. I stand in faith and agree that my family and I will know your love, peace, forgiveness, healing, and hope. Touch us everywhere we hurt. I claim our Victory now, In Jesus name – Amen!

3

Pushing Past the Pain: A Family's Journey Through Stigma and Grief
By Darlena Mays

According to research, approximately 80% of people with a mental illness feel their mental health conditions have detrimentally affected their families.[16] I can definitely agree that my family and I were intensely impacted by my nephew's illness. When my nephew's mental health symptoms escalated, he withdrew from the family and his social contacts. He began living on the streets. Months went by before I heard he was spotted in the community. People who saw him said he looked very tired and dirty. Hearing this news pained me. What was he eating and where was he sleeping? Was he in any danger out there and what about his clothes and bathing? These questions haunted me daily and not knowing was the worse. I missed him dearly, and I longed just to hear his voice or just to know he was safe.

His absence left a huge hole in my heart. I could not understand how a young man so full of potential and life could become so withdrawn. I questioned myself all the time and wondered what I had done to cause him to separate himself. Were there signs that I missed or failed to notice because I was so caught up in my own life challenges? For many of us in the family, we were perplexed and confused about how this happened, why it happened, and what we could do to help. Yet, many times, we felt lost and uncertain about what to say or do to help.

One major challenge I had in supporting my nephew was learning how to acknowledge and confront my own beliefs and fears of people with mental illness. Not only does society have stigmatizing beliefs about people with psychological diagnoses, but also family members can hold these beliefs as well. I remember when I finally saw my nephew for the first time after he had been living on the streets for months. I was hesitant to embrace him. I loved him and missed him, yet I feared the stench of the streets would get on me. I worried about if he had contracted any diseases while living on the streets and if these diseases would jump on me. I did hug him eventually and cried like a baby. As I held him, I forgot about all the things I had been worried about and just loved on my nephew.

These concerns resurfaced when he asked to stay with us for a few nights. Although my husband and I said yes, I found myself unable to sleep the nights my nephew was at our home. I worried about what he was doing in the other part of the house. I worried that he would leave and forget to close the front door. He also smoked cigarettes - would he forget to put one out and cause a fire? I believe these worries partly were fueled by the negative stigma towards people with mental illness. Many times people living with a mental health diagnosis are believed to be unstable, unpredictable, irresponsible, and dangerous. I witnessed how some of these views manifested in my worries about if I could truly trust him in my home. I also feel that these concerns were the result of several unknowns – I did not know who my nephew was *now*. I did not know what his diagnosis was, what he was capable of, or what he could be trusted to do. All of these things converged to create an atmosphere of anxiety and apprehension for my family and me.

One essential factor to truly supporting loved ones with mental illness is recognizing and admitting your own misperceptions about mental illness. The more I spent time around my nephew I came to realize that although some of my concerns were valid and reflective of his newfound limitations, some of my concerns were due to my limited understanding of mental illness. Because of this lack of knowledge, I was susceptible to negative and inaccurate views of people with mental illness. I would strongly encourage family members to seek out organizations, groups, and/or resources about mental illness in order to raise their awareness about mental health-related knowledge. Only then, can families correctly help their loved ones and fight against prejudice and discrimination against people living with psychological conditions.

Another strategy that helped me confront my misperceptions about mental illness was focusing on the similarities between my nephew and me. When we encounter people who are different, either because of race, gender, or mental health status, it is easy to fall into this trap of "us" and "them." This "us" vs. "them" mentality emphasizes the dissimilarities that exists between us. It was tempting to focus on all of the things that made my nephew different – his odor, his declining hygiene and grooming, his paranoid thoughts – however, I started to think about the ways in which he and I were similar. Soon before my nephew experienced declines in his mental health, I was diagnosed with cancer. Because of my cancer diagnosis, I could relate to his isolation. I too at times felt very isolated. I felt like I was all alone in this world and no one really understood my pain or what I was dealing with. I knew what it was like to suffer in silence and to wonder, "How do I handle the pain that no one can see but that follows me around every day and everywhere I go?" Cancer is not stigmatized like mental illness; yet, people can and do treat you differently because of the diagnosis. Many times, people did not know what to say to me or how to treat me. I could sense their feelings of powerlessness and concern, and this would increase my feelings of discomfort. In addition, in many people's minds, I became my diagnosis. Often, I felt that when people looked at me, they saw my diagnosis and not me, "Darlena." I detested how this felt, and I did not want to do this to my nephew. Drawing from these experiences, I was able to try to put myself in his shoes, and my heart grew in empathy and compassion for how he must have felt.

I strongly urge family and friends to make it a point to open their hearts to compassion and empathy concerning their loved one with mental illness. This is really what they need. Compassion is becoming aware of our shared humanity with others, and it literally means to "to suffer with."[17] In my case, I recognize that cancer and mental illness are different, but I also realized that my nephew and I both shared the experience of feeling pain, hurt, and rejection from others because of our diagnoses. This brought me closer to my nephew, and it helped me come to a place of healing concerning my own experiences and the hurt I felt about my nephew's situation.

Not only did my family and I have to grapple with our views about people with psychological concerns, but also we had to work through the grief we felt at losing the nephew we knew before the illness. Dealing with the reality of his mental illness was an extremely painful and traumatic time for my family and me. For me especially, it was difficult to come to terms with the reality of his illness because these new behaviors and symptoms were in such contrast to how I remembered him. When he was in elementary and middle school, our two families lived together. He was always such a warm and affectionate young man. He would always like to cuddle under his mom or be in her presence. We would tease him about being such a big momma's boy, and he could care less. He would lay across her lap and ask her to rub his ears or massage his scalp. He loved his mom's attention and craved one-on-one time with her, and she always obliged and welcomed it. Even when I hugged him for the first time after he returned from living on the streets, I was surprised by his hesitancy to embrace me. We were so close before, and I had loved him as my own son. Yet, he had become very distant and reserved. He wanted to keep to himself. He was disconnected from the relationship I had been so accustomed to having with him.

Grief is a common emotion prompted by loss. People usually think grief is experienced after the death of a loved one, but it can refer to any kind of loss. According to psychological research, coping with loss and grief is one of the hardest challenges people face. In the 1960s, psychiatrist Elisabeth Kübler-Ross proposed five common stages of grief: denial, anger, bargaining, depression, and acceptance. Denial occurs when we first find out about the loss. We tend to feel numb or shocked, and we question if the loss is real. Some of my family members stayed in denial for quite some time. One way this manifested was not accepting that my nephew had a mental illness. Some of us thought it was a "phase" or something that would be fixed by a hospital stay. We did not realize that his behavior and lack of motivation to spend time with family had become our new way of life. Also, the loss was particularly confusing and complicated because my nephew was still alive. He was physically present, but the person we once knew was absent. The denial phase is followed by anger, which occurs when the reality of the situation sets in. This phase can also include feelings of frustration and helplessness. I think some of us were angry that this happened again. We already had another nephew with mental health challenges, and we could not believe it was happening to another one of our loved ones. Bargaining follows anger, and it is during this stage that people ruminate on all the things they feel they could have done to prevent the loss from occurring. This is the stage where we replay the "What ifs." This was a difficult stage for me because I constantly questioned myself about if I had missed the mark and failed him by not noticing the signs sooner. Depression is the fourth stage, and feelings of sadness arise when the truth and reality of the loss set in. The final stage, acceptance, refers to our ability to accept the reality of the loss. It is only in accepting the loss that we can start moving forward with our life.

Throughout my experiences, I have learned that it is important for families to grieve. Grief, even if unattended, does not go away. Therefore, not making room to grieve in a healthy way can lead to complicated grief – grief that is persistent and impairing.[18] Although each person may have their own unique grieving process, some strategies to cope with grief are leaning on your faith, joining a support group, and talking with a grief counselor or therapist. For me, this process has taken time, but my family and I are the better because of it.

4

Stepping Up to the Plate: Choosing to Support Loved Ones with Mental Illness

By Valerie Watson-Smith

On a quiet summer night, my family's life changed forever. The day started like any other Saturday night; we were winding down from a long week, appreciative of the sanctuary of home. My husband and I were upstairs watching TV, and my parents were relaxing downstairs. We were enjoying this time because we knew the next day was Sunday, and we would be waking up early for church.

Around 11:30pm, we heard the doorbell ring. At first, I thought it was a sound from the TV. Then, this person proceeded to bang on our door. We became alarmed. Who could it be and what could they possibly want at this hour? My husband and father both cautiously went to the door. To their surprise and shock, it was my nephew. He was frantic! He had driven all the way to our house from where he lived, which was 1.5 hours away. I came to the door to inquire about the commotion. I was surprised and stunned to see him. He was talking loudly, he was pacing, and he appeared anxious. This was NOT the happy, go-lucky, jovial, and upbeat young man I knew. Something had changed; something seemed different. Given his behavior, our first thought was something terrible must have occurred. Was his mom (my sister) ok? Had something happened to his older brother?

Before this incident, we had not seen my nephew for some time except for holidays or special family gatherings. His parents had separated and were moving towards divorce. Although we knew his parents' divorce was a difficult time for him, we brushed off his sporadic absence as typical teenage behavior. None of us expected, or were prepared for, the reality of what was taking place in his life.

When he started talking coherently, he mentioned that someone had been following him as he drove on the freeway. Because of this, he drove quickly to escape. We did not know what to think. Was somebody really after him? Were they trying to harm him? Who were they? What did they want? I was fearful and alarmed! Clearly, he was in a panic, and we thought it best for him to stay the night with us. That night he refused to sleep in our spare bedroom upstairs. He slept near the front door to make sure our alarm was on, the deadbolts were secure, and the chain was firmly on the door. He took the batteries out of his phone. He was certain somebody was out to get him.

This event set the stage for us to invite my nephew to move into our home for six months. At the time, I did not have the knowledge of how mental illness manifested nor did I have the language to accurately describe what was going on with him. However, I knew something was wrong, and I could not quite put my finger on it. I was troubled in my emotions and in my spirit, and I began to pray and seek God for insight and understanding. I have always been an observant person, and my instincts moved me to intervene.

After a few days, my nephew settled into our place. He appeared more relaxed, but he still was not himself. One beautiful afternoon while I was at home on the computer, I felt led to stop working and to go talk to him. I told him I wanted to do a check-in to see how he was doing. We sat in the loft upstairs talking, and during our conversation, I realized things were more serious than I originally thought or wanted to believe. He shared that he still believed people were after him; these beliefs were so intense that he felt he needed to carry a weapon to protect himself. He mentioned he was hearing voices. He shared that he was afraid to leave our house, and the only time he left was to return to his house to pack more clothes.

This conversation was one of the most difficult experiences of my life. For any parent or relative who has to come to terms with the realization that something is different with their child or loved one, it is traumatic and heartbreaking. I was weeping and shaking on the inside, but I had to be strong on the outside. After that conversation, I was haunted by various questions: Was there something wrong or broken in my family line? How did we miss it? How long had this been happening? Were we too busy to notice?

In retrospect, I know now that I was witnessing developing signs of mental illness. However, mental illness was the last thing I suspected. For one, mental illness is not openly discussed in most families. There is stigma associated with it, and no one wants to believe it affects his or her loved one. Also, I did not want to believe that our family was being affected in this way again. The battle of mental illness and substance abuse had affected other family members, even though our family had a lineage of ministers, church leaders, deacons, and religious believers. Mental illness was the elephant in the room that many of us did not acknowledge or discuss.

I am a firm believer in divine and defining moments. God had me at the right place at the right time. It was this moment that allowed me to look into my nephew's eyes and to observe his behavior; to pay attention to the tone of his voice and the fear and uncertainty in his eyes. Something needed to be done to save my nephew, but I had to make myself available for this process to occur. From this process, I learned invaluable lessons. First, even though my nephew is not my biological son, he is my family; there is a bond between us. I knew I had to step up and to be the conduit for his recovery. I had to be the one to recognize the mental turmoil and anguish taking place in his mind. Second, I learned the importance of *really* checking-in with loved ones. We can easily become caught up in the busyness of life, but I had to decide to not let being busy keep me from checking in on my nephew. On any given day if someone were to ask me if I valued family I would answer, "Yes!" Nevertheless, this encounter truly challenged me to show up and live according to this value. I often think about what would have happened if I had not stopped what I was doing and followed my instincts to go talk to him. Third, this experience taught me the importance of listening. Although part of me wanted to challenge him – to convince him his beliefs and the voices were not real – in that moment I knew that if I did, he would put up a guard. Thus, I had to be willing to talk to him on his level, and to enter his world so that he knew he was not alone.

In the end, stepping up to facilitate my nephew's recovery was not easy. It took a lot of emotional, physical, and financial resources. However, I truly believe that it was the right thing to do, and if I had to do it over again, I would. Eventually though, the time came when we could no longer be there for him in the same way. As his symptoms progressed, it became glaringly clear that he needed professional help. He needed something to balance out his behavior, his mood swings, and temperament. He needed to be in a facility that could help him get better. This does not mean that we no longer had a role to play as his family, but rather it meant that our roles in his recovery process shifted.

Stepping up to help a loved one with a mental health diagnosis can look differently depending on the stage of their recovery. In our experience, our roles were to notice the signs, rally the family, and to initiate his treatment within a facility. Our home was also his safe haven in between hospital stays. Despite these myriad ways in which we stepped up, assisting a loved one with psychological concerns ultimately requires love, compassion, and presence, which is something our family continues to strive to provide our nephew with each passing day.

5

Navigating Rocky Terrain: Tough Decisions Encountered When Supporting Loved Ones with Mental Illness

By Teresa A. Tate

&

Valerie Watson-Smith

"My Voice" is that of a mother who has a son with a mental health diagnosis. My son was diagnosed with a mental illness in 2010, and although I noticed gradual shifts in my son's behavior, receiving the actual diagnosis led to a flurry of emotions. I felt guilt, shame, disbelief, fear, anger, and grief. I turned to God in prayer, and cried out. Yet, despite my disbelief, anguish, and pain, I had to show up and make some tough decisions.

When your loved one has a mental illness, you often find yourself in a place where you have to make difficult choices. Some of those choices include when and how to engage your loved one in treatment, who to involve in your loved one's recovery, and how to prevent relapse. This process can be frustrating, humiliating, and discouraging. In addition, when you are trying to successfully maneuver the mental health system, there is bureaucracy and tremendous red tape coupled with limited treatment options, and a lack of appropriate local and governmental resources, such as adequate programs and housing for people living with mental illness. Unfortunately, no one prepared me to navigate these decisions, especially while trying to manage life, work, and the various emotions I experienced along the way. Yet, with my family's help, God's grace, and the expertise of trained mental health professionals, I was able to navigate this path – a path I never imagined I would have to traverse. Here are some lessons I learned along the way.

Psychiatric Hospitalization

One of the most challenging choices my family and I had to make occurred when my son was in "total crisis mode." His behavior escalated to the point where he would disappear for days at a time. For instance, one day when he was at the family business helping out, he said he had to leave for a moment, and we did not see him for five days. I was frantic! His father and I called and texted multiple times, but we heard no response. By day two, I decided to text him to let him know about my plan to file a missing person's report if I did not hear back from him. He finally responded with a simple text, "Call you later." From that point on I knew something else was going on. Later that week, we received a call from the local authorities at 2:00 am. They informed us that they found our son in his car, in front of the family business, and we needed to come get him. When his father and uncle arrived, he was highly confused in his thoughts, he had not bathed in days, he was wearing the clothes we had last seen him in, and he was very afraid that someone was after him. At this point, it was clear that my son needed mental health assistance.

As a family of faith, we were accustomed to handling situations with prayer alone. Also, from a cultural standpoint, it was expected that issues involving loved ones were taken care of within the family. However, this was different! We knew it was time to reach outside of our comfort-zone of resources, outside of our religious affiliation, and to seek professional mental health services and support. This did not mean that prayer was not an effective tool, but that for what we were up against, we were going to need every tool in the box.

Because of this, we decided to initiate a voluntary psychiatric inpatient hospitalization. A psychiatric inpatient hospitalization is when someone is admitted to the psychiatric unit of the hospital for observation. The length of stay can vary, but it is not an indefinite confinement. Most individuals with a mental health diagnosis will not require time in the hospital or treatment center due to psychiatric reasons during their lifetime;[19] however, given the nature of my son's symptoms, our best option was a psychiatric inpatient hospitalization. This allowed him to be closely monitored, and it led him to be accurately diagnosed. With the diagnosis came clarity and a deeper understanding of his experiences, both for himself and for the family. While in the hospital, he was able to attend individual meetings and group sessions to learn more about his symptoms and diagnosis as well as effective coping skills to use when he was released from the hospital. Additionally, during his hospitalization, he was placed on appropriate medication and stabilized. His hospitalization allowed him the time to solely concentrate on recovering from his mental health crisis.

Timing

One of the things that made my son's psychiatric inpatient hospitalization successful was timing. When his behavior started to spiral, we initiated his hospitalization as quickly as possible. We moved swiftly because we were anxious my son would change his mind, although he knew he needed help. Had we waited or been overly caught up in the intense emotions, stigma, and shock, we could have missed our opportunity to successfully engage him in treatment. A missed opportunity could have resulted in a worse outcome for everyone involved.

We moved rapidly, but it was not easy. Although I was totally engaged in the process, I could not physically take my son to the hospital for his admission. Emotionally, I could not "catch up" to what I understood logically needed to be done. As a mother, the pain was too great, and the emotions were too intense. I could not fathom my son having to be separated from his family, his surroundings, and his comforts. I was plagued by not knowing for certain if he would be okay. As a mother, you feel as if your one job is to protect your children, and here it was I felt completely helpless as my son endured this crisis. Thankfully, my sister and brother-in-law stepped in and facilitated this process with my son; they served as key players in this process.

Key Players

Despite the anguish of having to admit my son for a psychiatric inpatient hospitalization, the effectiveness was due to key players – reliable persons who stepped in to assist during this time of need. Key players are individuals who can provide an array of support and who can help execute and carryout crisis and/or stabilization plans. This is important because, as in my situation, there may come a time when there is something you cannot physically, logistically, or emotionally handle on your own. Often families that care for loved ones with mental illness withdraw from their support networks because of shame, embarrassment, or simply the burden of taking care of their loved one. However, it is important to maintain contact with those networks as they can provide much needed comfort, support, and assistance.

Key players can be immediate family members or members of your village family community (e.g., church members, family friends, colleagues). It is important to keep in mind that although you may have many people in your circle, key players need to be individuals your loved one *trusts*. Because of this, not everyone in your circle may be able to serve as a key player. For instance, when my son was discharged from the hospital, some of my family members immediately started encouraging my son to go back to work. Although they meant well and truly cared about my son's future, they did not understand that these types of comments created additional stress for him. Although going back to work could have been an option for him eventually, the timing and approach of their comments added to his stress instead of alleviating it. Similarly, at times when my son's thinking became confused, I observed family members try to dissuade my son from thinking in that way. Again, although I believe they were truly trying to help, these attempts caused my son to feel further isolated, invalidated, and misunderstood. As a result, he further withdrew from the family, except from those key individuals with whom he felt most comfortable.

Special training is not required to be a key player. However, there are wonderful national resources (see the references provided at the end of the book) available for those who assist individuals with mental illness. Some skills that can be useful when working with individuals with mental health diagnoses are social skills training, de-escalation strategies, suicide support, and empathy building. I would encourage everyone who supports someone living with a mental health condition to learn more about these skills in order to provide care that is sensitive and responsive to their unique needs.

Key Partners

Key players are individuals who provide support in the day-to-day recovery process whereas key partners are mental health professionals who assist in times of a mental health crisis and/or contribute to consultation, relapse prevention planning, and medication adherence strategies. My experience has taught me the importance of building and establishing a partnership between my key players and professional mental health workers (e.g., psychiatrists, psychologists, social workers, and nurses). This partnership has been very helpful in ensuring my son receives quality care and assistance.

First, this partnership made sure everyone was on the same page with regard to the goals for my son's treatment. This was especially the case when we decided to initiate medication use for my son. At first, I was leery of psychiatric medications; I did not want my son to be overly medicated to where he was no longer himself. He, too, was concerned about the effects of the medication. However, the mental health professionals were able to provide us with vital information regarding the benefits of medication for his particular symptoms. They also cared about our concerns and introduced a plan where they would introduce a lower dosage and only increase the dosage if necessary. Therefore, we agreed to the important role of medication in my son's treatment plan, but also we were on the same page about the essential role of him being able to feel like himself and to maintain his unique personality.

Second, this partnership provided an appreciation for everyone's expertise. For instance, the family members and I who were responsible for my son's care on a daily basis had valuable information to provide the mental health professionals who were working with my son. We could inform them if he took his medication consistently and the side effects observed. Also, the mental health professionals were able to provide insight so that we would realistically adjust our expectations for my son's behavior.

Third, this partnership facilitated necessary advocacy for my son, especially during times when my family and I felt "stuck" due to the bureaucracy within the mental health system. I remember one of the first calls I made to a clinical social worker. I talked to her about my son, what he was going through, how this was very new for our family, and how I did not know what to do. Her actual words to me were, "I normally don't get involved with a patient's treatment plan or involved with their case manager, but I knew this was a good kid who came from a good family who'd lost his way and just needed some help to get back on track." From this conversation, she became a vital partner and resource for my son and I. She began to assist us by contacting my son's case manager in order to advocate on my son's behalf so he could obtain the best treatment plan for his diagnosis and individual goals.

Throughout this relationship, it was essential that mutual trust and agreement existed between the mental health professionals, my village family, and I. This relationship began while my son was in the hospital, but since his initial release, we have continued periodic contact. This allowed us to ensure my son progressed through his mental health journey successfully.

Plan for Relapse

Each of these decisions are tough in their own right, but planning for possible relapse was especially difficult. It required a re-conceptualization of what mental illness was and was not. Although I had heard the term mental illness and had seen images in the media about individuals with mental illness, I did not have much professional knowledge about the different types of symptoms and outcomes associated with each mental health diagnosis. As a result, part of me expected that, once we made it through this hurdle and mental health crisis, everything would return to normal. However, this was not our experience.

When my son was released from the hospital, it took him a while to acclimate into his normal routine, but after some time, he radically improved. The gleam in his face and eyes, that had been absent for months, returned. Because he previously went to school to become a certified healthcare worker, we were excited when he found a job in the healthcare field. This inspired him to set additional goals: to get his own apartment and a new car. He was overjoyed when his father and I stepped in to assist him. We helped him find a new apartment, and after some months of working, he purchased a new car. He was on his way! The old, fun-loving, charismatic person was back. These joys were also experienced among the family – life was good! Our family could breathe and exhale.

About two years later, his world came crashing down, and this time it was worse. I believe the pressure from working long hours, not getting enough rest, and handling new financial obligations due to his new apartment and car led to stress, which then led to his setback. This setback resulted in another psychiatric inpatient hospitalization.

Relapse occurs when "troubling symptoms come back or get worse" [20] especially after temporary improvement. We had "strong faith" that a relapse would not occur, and it was important for us to believe in my son's ability to recover. Research shows that a family's belief in loved ones with mental illness makes a huge difference.[21] Yet, we have learned through experience that relapses are possible. According to psychological research, relapses are often a natural phase of the mental health recovery process. For instance, relapse rates for depression are reportedly as high as 80%.[22] For schizophrenia, the relapse rate is about 80% within 2 years if medication is discontinued, and only about 40% for recovered patients who adequately take their medication as prescribed.[23] Given the nature of my son's diagnosis, the reality and possibility of relapse was quite likely. One of the difficult lessons for my family and I has been to understand that mental illness is not like a cold; it does not just go away. Although it is possible for someone to experience a depressive episode and never experience clinical depression again, most mental health disorders are chronic; they are lifelong disorders that have to be effectively managed in order for individuals to live successfully.

Realistically, symptoms can reappear at any time. Some common early signs of relapse are changes in mood, changes in sleep patterns, increased irritability, increased difficulty concentrating, social withdrawal, and decreased motivation to engage in personal care (e.g., grooming).[24] There are also certain factors that put individuals at risk for relapse. First, loved ones are most at risk for relapse when they are dealing with overwhelming stress.[25] Stress is a normal part of life; no one can escape it. However, it is important for individuals to have effective coping strategies to use when they encounter stress. Effective coping strategies include prayer, journaling, listening to music, exercise, and problem solving skills. Also, attending individual and group therapy can be life changing. Second, a key factor that can bring about relapse is lack of sleep or irregular sleep. This is what happened in my son's case. Because of his work schedule and the increased stress he experienced, his sleeping patterns became irregular. Third, a vital factor with regards to relapse is discontinuing medication and/or using medication inconsistently, especially when you feel better. [26] Often, when individuals experience improvement in their symptoms, they feel they no longer need medication. However, the improvement in symptoms is likely due to taking the medication consistently and as prescribed. Thus, discontinuing medication without a doctor's supervision can cause symptoms to return. Fourth, relapse can occur when individuals are not aware of or are not paying attention to certain triggers. Although there are common relapse signs, it is also important that families and mental health professionals communicate about the loved one's individual signs of relapse in order to bring about an early treatment intervention.

Given our experiences with my son, we decided to be proactive and create a relapse plan in the event that he experienced another relapse. As my son's mother, I asked my family and my village family members to pay close attention to any sudden or gradual changes in my son's moods, thinking patterns, and behaviors. If they did notice changes, I asked them to call it to his father's or my attention so we could initiate contact with our team of mental health professionals, if necessary. With this plan in place, my family and I were able to collectively intervene when we noticed my son slipping back into old unhealthy routines and patterns. I believe planning for relapse allowed us to have a realistic sense of what to expect and how to respond when necessary.

Full Time Housing

When my son was discharged from his first psychiatric inpatient hospitalization, we agreed that he would temporarily move in with my sister, brother-in-law, and parents whose home had an extra bedroom. Although I would have preferred for my son to live with me, I did not have adequate space. He thrived while he lived with my family; living with them provided him structure, social connection, and safety. During this time, he occasionally helped out at the family business, which gave him a sense of purpose and meaning. Things got to the point where he felt he was able to live independently, and his father and I supported this. We were happy to see my son energized, motivated, and inspired to get back to living his life. As mentioned in the above section, he obtained his own apartment, and he went back to work. Life was good, and he was well on his way to recovery.

However, after about two years, he ended up in the psychiatric hospital again. After several days, he was stabilized. Given that it worked the first time, we decided that, once discharged, he would return to live with my sister, brother-in-law, and parents. Yet, after approximately six months, the time came when my family could no longer house him full time. As he lived with them, it became glaringly clear that he needed to be in a place where he could receive additional therapeutic support, like group counseling, case management services, and individual support. Although my family loved him and desired to support him as best they could, because of their work schedules, they could not assist him with day-to-day living tasks, like budgeting, grocery shopping, meal planning, and taking medication, which is essential for a loved one in recovery. Further, we were worried about him having too much time unattended at their home while they were at work. As a result, we desired for him to get into a facility that could help him improve. We looked into residential facilities that could provide him with support services and repeated contacts; but it was also important that the environment was not too restrictive. We wanted our son to maintain some semblance of independence so that he could establish his own normal living rhythm. Yet, a main barrier to this was that he did not want to live anywhere other than my family's home nor did he think he needed psychological assistance. As a result, he ended up living on the streets. This led to another difficult decision: respect for autonomy.

Respect Autonomy

Things were much more difficult after my son's second psychiatric hospitalization. Eventually things progressed to the point where he ended up living on the streets. He refused to stay at transitional housing programs, and after multiple failed attempts to live with friends, he ended up living on the streets. This was one of the most difficult times for me, because most of the time, I did not know where he was. People who knew me and my family would tell us when they saw him walking in different parts of town; some even shared that they had seen him standing in front of stores asking for money. Often, I would drive around town, hoping I would see him. There were times I did; some days he looked good, and other days, he did not look well. When I would try to get him to come home with me, he would refuse. He seemed to find solitude in the streets. The streets were not my choice for him. Yet, I had to come to terms with the fact that my son was an adult. Although my family and I desired more for him, we had to accept his personal choices.

Throughout this process, I wanted to fix it. I also wanted God to hurry up and fix it. However, I had to learn patience. I had to be patient with my son, with myself, with God, and with the process. I could not rush my son's recovery or pressure him to do anything he was unwilling to do even if I felt I knew best.

Respecting your loved one's autonomy can take various forms depending on where he or she is in the recovery process. For me, it took the form of having to accept my son's decision to live on the streets, but for some, it may be simply learning to respect your loved one's boundaries. At the end of the day, your loved one is his/her own person. By respecting boundaries, you are making yourself available when he or she is ready to accept your help, but you are not hovering or nagging. Another way you can respect your loved one's boundaries is by asking what he or she needs; do not assume what is needed. Instead of asking, "Did you take your medication?", ask if you can give medication reminders. Ask if he or she needs help with daily tasks or if he or she would like additional support at health care appointments.

In September 2016, my patience paid off. My son showed up at the home of my parents, sister, and brother-in-law. He told them he was tired and he wanted to come back home. Because they always loved him, supported him, and created an atmosphere of acceptance, he knew they would embrace him with open arms. Today, things are still in process, and we are still figuring out many things along the way; however, I am grateful God eventually led him back home.

6

Confronting Stigma: When Mental Illness Comes to Your Door

By Teresa A. Tate
&
Dr. Natalie Watson-Singleton

Mental illness does not discriminate. It does not care if you are a man or woman, rich or poor, or identify as Christian, Jewish, Muslim, or Agnostic. Although there are misperceptions about who experiences mental illness, it affects one in five adults.[27] Yet, despite the pervasiveness of mental illness, many people do not understand it. This lack of information leads to inaccurate beliefs about mental illness, its causes, and its effects. For instance, people are twice as likely today than they were in 1950 to believe people with mental illness are more violent than the general public; yet, people with mental health diagnoses are 2.5 times more likely to be *victims* of violence than members of the general population.[28] Further, research has found that 68% of Americans did not want someone with a mental illness marrying into their family. Similarly, 58% of Americans reported they did not want someone with a mental illness in their workplace.[29]

Based on these staggering statistics, it is clear that people with psychological diagnoses face insurmountable stigma.

Stigma is defined as disapproval and shame felt by individuals who display thoughts, emotions, behaviors, and characteristics deemed wrong or unusual by society.[30] According to Dr. Patrick Corrigan, an acclaimed psychology professor and expert in mental health stigma research, there are two common types of stigma that affect people with mental illness: public stigma and self-stigma.[31] On the one hand, public stigma refers to society's reaction towards people with mental illness. For example, an employer may not hire someone with mental illness because he believes that person is incapable of producing satisfactory work. On the other hand, self-stigma has to do with the prejudice people with mental illness turn against themselves. For instance, persons with mental illness may believe they are incapable of working because they internalize beliefs that they are not valuable members of society.

As a mother, it has been difficult to witness the stigma surrounding my son. I have observed that his mental health concerns are not treated with the same sensitivity and tolerance as physical ailments. For instance, when individuals have heart issues, society does not tell them to "just get over it." Yet, society expects people with psychological concerns to "snap" out of their symptoms.

Not only has stigma concerns been palpable for my son, but they have also affected me. I am not alone in this experience. Psychological researchers have even coined the term, "family stigma"[32] to denote the stigma that impacts an individual's family members. Family stigma can operate in a variety of ways. First, family members may feel particularly stigmatized due to the role of genetics in mental illness. Although genetics do not fully account for disorders, research does support a genetic predisposition for most mental health diagnoses.[33] As a result, family members may feel that if their loved one demonstrates signs and symptoms of mental illness, then others may think the family members too are more genetically predisposed to mental illness. Although I never personally felt that others assumed I had mental illness, I would often find myself struggling with questions as to why it seemed like various family members experienced similar issues. The battle of mental illness and substance abuse was prevalent in our family, and it became an elephant in the room that could not be ignored. I would wonder if something was "wrong" with our family. Second, we as family members can feel stigmatized because others blame us for our loved one's symptoms. Whether it is because of something the family did or did not do, often people look to the family as the root cause of the disorder. For me, I often heard things like, "He (my son) hasn't been the same since the divorce." Although there is truth in the fact that the divorce between my son's father and I deeply hurt our son, this statement highlighted others' beliefs that my son's father and I were to blame for our son's challenges. This was extremely hurtful for us as we were already coping with the difficult emotions that come with divorce. One thing that has been healing in overcoming this stigma and the opinions of others is educating myself about mental illness. Yes, genetics and family environments play a role in the development and maintenance of diagnoses, but these disorders are much too complex to be explained by just one or two factors. Therefore, my son's mental illness is the result of multiple, interacting factors, and it cannot be simply reduced to one or two events.

Something I've also found interesting is, although having a family member with mental illness can lead to unique stigmatizing encounters for family members, these experiences are most visible in social spheres.[34] One social sphere in which this stigma can be strongest is within faith communities. Research has demonstrated that families of someone with a mental illness reported feeling less accepted in their religious communities.[35] This has been especially true for me as a woman of faith, but also as a leader in my religious community. I have witnessed the church primarily handle mental illness by either ignoring it or over-spiritualizing it.[36]

One reason I feel mental illness has been largely ignored in faith communities is because of the tendency to exclusively treat mental illness as a spiritual problem. Although I believe one's physical, mental, and spiritual health are interconnected and equally valuable, it is imperative for church communities to properly educate themselves about the nature of mental illness. I belong to a religious community, and in these contexts I would hear people characterize my son's condition and others mental illness as "primarily a spiritual or religious issue." When I would hear this type of comment, it would make me feel isolated, confused, and stigmatized. Had I not educated myself about the complex nature of mental illness, I could have easily fallen prey to believing my son's symptoms were simply the result of a spiritual defect. This could have easily lead to unwise treatment recommendations, such as rejecting psychological services or discontinuing medication without a doctor's supervision.

In the absence of accurate information, communities, like religious settings, can create alternative narratives about the root causes of mental illness, which are not always reflective of science and personal realities. Also, I think it is human nature to struggle with uncertainty; therefore, because we do not know everything about mental illness, we over-spiritualize things.

However, this tendency to over-spiritualize implies that our faith is not big enough to handle incomprehensible problems. This directly contradicts what it means to be a person of faith. I love the phrase Amy Simpson puts forth in her article, *Mental illness: What is the church's role?* "Mental illness *does* raise challenging questions, but such questions do not threaten God."[10] This is a necessary reminder that God is big enough to handle everything we cannot grasp. It is better to embrace the things we cannot figure out and to place them in God's hands than to create misguided explanations and expectations that do more harm to ourselves and the ones we love. If you are struggling to understand the encounters you have faced when supporting your loved one, know that it is ok. Put it in God's hands, receive professional counsel, and resist the temptation to mask the unknown with faulty and simplified explanations.

Unfortunately, the Church's propensity to ignore the problem of mental illness furthers the stigma and isolation experienced by those who are affected. Rick Warren, Pastor of Saddleback Church located in Lake Forest, California also eloquently writes about this.[37] Pastor Warren's intimate knowledge of the highs and lows of mental illness came from supporting his son through mental health challenges – the son whom he later lost to suicide. Pastor Warren's son died by suicide five days after Easter Sunday in April 2013. Despite this devastating experience and his desire to hide from public scrutiny, Pastor Warren posed a thought-provoking question: "If your brain doesn't work right and you take a pill, why are you supposed to be ashamed of that?" It's just an organ, and we have to remove that stigma." I truly admire the courage it took for Pastor Warren to speak up and to speak out against stigma in the midst of the heartbreaking experience of his son's suicide. Pastor Warren later acknowledged, "Behind every publicly successful ministry, there is private pain. And, pain is

God's megaphone." [38] God wants to use our pain and suffering to minister to others who may be going through similar experiences. For many of us, our greatest purpose and impact in the lives of others will come out of our deepest hurts, disappointments, and setbacks. Those around us will not be impressed by how we handle the highs of life, but rather, how we handle its lows. However, when it comes to mental illness, for many of us, we desire to hide it away like our private shame. But the time is now for us to walk in the truth of our reality and to be silent no more.

This silence is also heightened for those of us who are leaders. In my role as a leader in both my religious and workplace contexts, I have observed that leaders follow a "non-verbal code" – we do not talk about mental illness for fear that those we lead may judge and perceive us, or our loved one, differently. For many leaders, I also think there is the fear our leadership acuity and ability will be threatened. Early on, in my own experience, I would withdraw and live out my reality in silence, plagued by the worry that the secret of my son's illness would be revealed. I often struggled with what to say and what not to say. For one, I did not want to bring negative attention to my son; at the end of the day, as his mother my number one desire was to protect him. In addition, I was doing all I could to just navigate my own leadership expectations with excellence. This meant balancing travel, program development, and clients' needs as well as the unexpected ongoing occurrences associated with my son's disease. I worried that if others knew about the ways I had to show up for my son, often unexpectedly, they would question my ability to handle my leadership responsibilities. Yet, keeping silent led to more stress and pressure to maintain the façade that everything was "fine." Eventually, the time came for me to remove the façade, and to open up about my life as a mom and leader who had a son with a mental health diagnosis.

Since coming out about my son's illness, I have had to dig-in much deeper and hone-in much greater to my foundational beliefs, principles of faith, and values. I had to square-off to face the pseudo-giants of guilt, shame, and fear that wanted me to remain silent. I knew if I wanted to live a life free from stigma, I was going to have to share my journey with others. Also, the silence was undermining my son's wellness and recovery, and it was hindering my ability to show up for him in the best ways possible. As you begin this walk to challenge stigma, I admonish you to first be honest with yourself about the realities of your loved one's illness. Know that their illness is not your fault, yet; you have a role to play in their recovery. As you are journeying down this road, I would also encourage you to partner with both local and national organizations that provide education about mental illness as well as advocacy for those affected by the illness. You cannot make it alone, and you do not have to make it alone. The time is now to stand up against shame, ignorance, and fear, and to bring about change and greater awareness to end the stigma against ourselves and our loved ones.

7

Letting Go Of Anger:
Making Peace with the Broken Pieces
By Teresa A. Tate

Several of the chapters in this book have referenced difficult emotions that arise when working through the reality of having a loved one with mental illness. Confronting these emotions is a normal part of coping with having a loved one with mental health concerns. According to the American Psychological Association (APA) – the largest scientific and professional psychology organization in the United States – it is common for family members to feel ashamed, hurt, or embarrassed by loved ones with psychological conditions.[39] In addition, I have learned that these emotions can compound to produce supplementary feelings of anger.

Anger is a basic human emotion that everyone experiences. According to the Merriam Webster dictionary, anger is "an intense emotional state of displeasure with someone or something." Anger is usually triggered by an emotional hurt or situation in which we have been injured, mistreated, or opposed in attaining our goals.[40] I always thought I understood anger, but I have come to learn that the experience of anger varies widely from person to person. People differ in how often they experience anger, how intensely they feel anger, and how long their anger lasts. This raw emotion also affects how families cope with having a loved one with psychological concerns.

My "a-ha" moments about anger occurred on a very late Friday night. I was reading notes for this book chapter, and as I sat quietly asking for divine guidance, I started to reflect on my own anger and why it had not been resolved. Then I started to think about the key ingredients needed to move to the other side of anger. Here are some "Basic Truths" that have proven real in my personal life:

- You must confront feelings of anger regarding your loved one's mental illness
- You must let go of the need for things to be different than they are in this moment
- You must make peace with the broken pieces

Basic Truth #1: You must confront feelings of anger regarding your loved one's mental illness

As a mother and a woman, it was not easy to acknowledge the anger I felt about my son's illness. Whereas most men express their anger outwardly, many women suppress their anger because it is viewed as an emotion that is not "feminine." I was angry at life – angry that I had been dealt another unfair blow concerning my children. I had lost my firstborn daughter when she was just three-months old due to Sudden Infant Death Syndrome. It took decades for me to come to terms with my daughter's death, so how was it that I was now in danger of losing my son as I knew him? I could not wrap my head around how God could let this happen to me again. Moreover, although I was not initially angry with my son nor did I blame him for his illness, as the months progressed, I became angry with him as I watched him resist treatment and reject our family's help. There were days when it seemed like we cared more about his well-being and future than he did. This left me feeling alone, hopeless, and wondering if things would ever change for the better.

Despite the fact that I was angry, it took me awhile to acknowledge this to myself. I had several questions, like "How is it that a mother, family member, or friend who loves their loved one so much still privately and internally struggle with anger?" I did not know how to reconcile the fact that love and anger could co-exist. Often times, we try to fit things into neat, black-and-white boxes. But, there are times in our lives where things are not neat; rather, they are complex, messy, and full of grey areas. My experiences taught me that the anger that I felt about my son's situation did not take away from the love I felt for him. In fact, I had to come to terms with the fact that it was okay for me to be angry and that being angry did not mean I was a bad mother. However, I could not remain angry. If I let anger fester, then it would compromise my ability to show up for my son repeatedly and constantly in love. Therefore, acknowledging this anger was essential for me to achieve emotional healing and wholeness and to be the mother I desired to be for my son.

On this journey, I also learned that acknowledging anger was not a one-time affair. It required vigilant practice every time new issues arose, like when my son would miss medication appointments or refuse additional outpatient support. I also had to guard my heart from the tendency to become stuck in the "why me" phase of anger during times when I would witness other parents celebrating their children's joyous milestones, like graduations and weddings. Overall, this basic truth has been a daily practice.

***Basic Truth #2: You must let go of the need for things to be
different than they are in this moment***

Working through anger also required that I "let God off the hook." What I mean by this is, as a spiritual person, I believe in prayer and God's control over the entire universe. I knew He had the power to prevent this circumstance from happening as well as the power to fix this situation in my life. So why did he let my son develop mental illness? Why had he not removed my son's illness after his first hospitalization when I cried out and begged Him to?

Coming to terms with my anger toward God and the anger I felt from His unwillingness to take away my son's illness and to do things on my timeline was a "biggie" for me as a leader in the faith community because there was a certain level of denial. First, I was in denial that I was even angry with God. I did not want to confront the reality that the God I served allowed me to hurt like this again. Second, I was in denial about the fact that someone who holds certain values and principles and has a deep devotion to faith could even have God on the hook. Logically, I knew God did not always do what we wanted Him to do when we wanted Him to do it. However, in my emotions, I was holding God hostage to my demands and timetable, and every time He did not do what I wanted when I wanted concerning my son, my anger amplified.

In order to let God "off the hook" and to resolve the anger I felt about things not going the way I wanted, I had to do three things: come to terms with the present (where we are today), relinquish the past (specifically any unrealistic goals or dreams I previously had for my son), and focus on creating new memories that fostered a fresher relationship. These steps were not easy. First, accepting the present was extremely difficult because it did not align with what I wanted and hoped for regarding my son and

I. Also, accepting the present meant I had to let go of the need for things to be different in this moment. Yet, many days I was not willing to let go of the need for things to be different because then I felt like I was giving up. However, letting go of the need for things to be different did not mean I was giving up; rather, it meant I was seeing things for what they really were. Only then could I move forward in an effective way. Second, relinquishing the past meant I had to let go of how things used to be as well as the need for my son to go back to the son he was before the illness. As a parent, this was particularly challenging because it meant also readjusting my hopes and expectations for my son's future. Third, focusing on creating new memories meant truly taking the time to explore and understand the limits and opportunities that come with mental illness. Having a mental illness is not a hopeless situation, and even though my son was not able to do some of the things he used to, there were still many things he could do. Therefore, our newfound relationship needed to be based on this new understanding of who he was and what he was capable of.

Overall, when I finally admitted my anger and disappointment regarding how I felt things could have been different or fixed I felt a weight lift off of me, and I experienced another level of peace.

Basic Truth #3: You must make peace with the broken pieces

The peace that overtook me after I worked the first two basic truths opened my eyes to the third basic truth: you must make peace with the broken pieces.

What do I mean by the term "broken pieces?" Broken pieces are either things that have caused intense pain and trauma or unresolved life-changing events that have caused negative reactions or responses in our lives. A broken piece example for me was the change I first saw in my son. To some people the changes were gradual, but for me the changes crashed down in one fell swoop to the point where I felt like he had begun to spiral down and spiral out within days. The huge, painful secret he had struggled with in silence – the secret he tried to manage, mask, and cope with alone – had now been brought to the light. This moment caused me intense pain and trauma and changed my life forever. I had to confront it, grieve it, and finally make peace with it, and that is exactly what I did! Because of that decision, I can definitely say that I am experiencing another level of freedom and wholeness in my emotions and in my state of being. To anyone reading this chapter and this book, I am very hopeful and confident that you too can take the forward steps in *making peace with the broken pieces.*

~

Since manifesting these three basic truths in my life, I have experienced several benefits. I have moved to a healthier place of living and being. I no longer feel like a victim to mental illness. I have acquired fresh creative passion, especially as it relates to creating projects aimed at helping other family and friends who have a loved one with a psychological diagnosis. This has resulted in a changed perspective, a new mind-set, and a newfound purpose.

8

Embracing the New Normal: Setting Realistic Expectations for Life with a Loved One with Mental Illness
By Teresa A. Tate

When I go back in my mind to when my son was younger, I remember him struggling to relax. I would say to him, "Calm yourself" or "Calm your spirit," encouraging him to self-soothe. Sometimes, if we were at home and he seemed stressed or anxious, I would let him lay his head on my lap. I would rub his forehead and talk to him, sing to him, and say a little prayer for him. When he was a teenager, he was still highly energized, and it remained a challenge for him to unwind. The difference was I also noticed he had trouble focusing for long periods of time (unless he was playing video-games), and his moods shifted more regularly. For the most part, I brushed this off as the phases and stages of "Teenage Boyhood." However, his thoughts, moods, and behaviors eventually became more unpredictable. We suspected that something was clearly wrong, but little did we know he was demonstrating the emerging signs of mental illness.

When I first learned of my son's mental health diagnosis, it felt like I was watching a bad movie or experiencing a bad dream. I remember saying to myself, "Eventually this part of the movie will be over," or "When I wake up, everything will be better and back to normal!" Well, neither was the case. What I had hoped would be a brief "commercial break" was actually the beginning of my new normal.

The term "new normal" is often used to characterize a new standard of what is to be expected or experienced.[41] In order to receive the new normal, we must replace past memories, routines, and experiences with what is necessary for our current reality. It means shifting from what used to be to how life is now. For me, in order to effectively support my son through his recovery, I had to let go of old habits and patterns of relating and interacting with him in order to engage in patterns that are reflective of how life is now. One example of this is how we communicate. When my son talks about beliefs and ideas that may reflect his paranoia, I do not get caught up in trying to challenge him. Rather, I focus on maintaining an open line of communication and simply appreciating that he feels comfortable sharing these things with me. I have learned, and I am still learning, how to make these changes, but in order for my son to walk in the fullness of his healing and recovery, it is imperative that I accept the reality that this is a new day, a new season, and our new normal.

Based on my own learning process, I had to do several things to establish and embrace a new normal. First, I had to come to terms with the fact that a new normal was necessary. I could not occupy the land of avoidance and denial. I could not act like, with time, things would go back to the way they used to be. When I discovered my son's diagnosis, I had two choices: sit on my hands and refuse to change or play the cards I was dealt. Although it was trying in every way imaginable, I chose to move forward and to make the best out of this new reality.

Second, I had to reconcile my current reality with my past. For me, this meant I had to first let go of the tendency to constantly compare my present life with what used to be. There would be times, especially on the extremely tough days with my son, when I would find myself reflecting about those moments we shared when he was younger as he laid his head in my lap. Although there was nothing wrong with me strolling through memory lane, I noticed that getting stuck on these memories left me feeling sad, disappointed, and resentful that things were no longer the way they used to be. I also had to come to terms with the fact that certain hopes I had for my son were no longer realistic. This did not mean I gave up on my son. It meant that I had to readjust my hopes and dreams for him to be more aligned with his current strengths and limitations instead of my own preconceived notions. Surprisingly, this was also beneficial for him. When I was able to openly acknowledge his current strengths and limitations, he no longer felt pressured to live up to the young man he used to be. He now had the space to forge a new life for himself, and he came to trust me to genuinely support him. Nevertheless, my dear readers, this has not been easy! In fact, there have been many days when I felt disappointed and let down – days when it took everything in my power to not succumb to the suffocating feelings of loss – the loss of the son I used to know and the life I used to live. I have also had to grieve the possibilities I so vividly fantasized about regarding how life would be for me and my family and me. In addition, although these experiences have been painful, they have allowed me to accept that my son has a mental health diagnosis and to come to terms with the truths of my present reality.

Once I went through the steps described above, I was able to arrive at a place of acceptance. Acceptance does not mean that you give up, throw your hands in the air, and walk away. Instead, acceptance means seeing things as they truly are and letting go of the insatiable desire for things to be different than they are in this moment. For me, I had to accept my son's diagnosis at both the emotional and intellectual level. Despite the challenges of acceptance, walking in acceptance has given me the freedom to create new memories built on a new foundation of truth. Also, by *truly* accepting the reality of my son's diagnosis and my life as a mom who had a son with a mental health diagnosis, I was able to welcome possibilities I had not previously considered. Writing this book is one example of this. I never imagined I would get to a place where I could share my story so openly and transparently. It was scary, and I felt extremely vulnerable and unsure about how it would be perceived and received. This book was birthed from the place of my pain and from the journey I endured (and am still enduring) to get to where I am now. It was also inspired by my own frustrations during this process – not feeling like there were enough satisfactory resources for me to turn to for hope, encouragement, and understanding. As I searched for information and answers, my perspective broadened as I learned that I was not alone; mental illness was impacting numerous families, workplaces, and communities. Through this, my voice as a mother, and as a voice for other mothers and family members emerged. Yet, this book, and my openness to learning about others' experiences, would not have happened had I hid away in the darkness of shame, guilt, and silence. *I had to make a choice to come out of darkness and step into the light of acceptance, and in so doing, God graced me to walk in new levels of peace and reconciliation.*

There were several reasons I was motivated to embrace my new normal. For one, it helped my community networks and I to remain flexible. One of the things I have learned on this journey is that my son's experience with mental illness can lead to unpredictable and unexpected situations and events. He has some good days, and he has some bad days, and that is the reality we must acknowledge and accept. Because of this, I am most effective when I focus on the *current* needs of my son, family, and those involved in his care. If I get too caught up on what he used to need or what used to work, I cannot effectively adapt to what is going on presently. Also, staying flexible prevents me from being "thrown off" when something does occur. Instead of perceiving unplanned situations as failures in recovery, I acknowledge them as par for the course.

A second reason is it allowed me to set realistic expectations for how my son, my family, and I functioned both in the short-term and in the long-term. Throughout my son's journey, my social networks have stepped up immensely to provide support. Initially, when a life-changing, traumatic event occurs, family and friends rally together to fix whatever is going on. But, it is also natural for that support to change over time, especially when the circumstance is on-going and prolonged. Because of this, I informed others that taking care of a loved one with mental illness involves a lifetime commitment. I knew it was imperative for me to communicate this to my networks so they could also adjust to the new normal. Having these conversations fostered a stronger connection between my support systems and I, increased our opportunities to have open and transparent conversations which ultimately promoted family cohesion and sustainability throughout this journey. Remember, it is a marathon not a sprint!

It has not been easy to ride the waves of the ups and downs of coming to terms with my new normal. Throughout my experience, I have discovered that just because I have done it once, there are times when I have to repeat and rehearse what I have learned, as well as to repeat and move through each of these phases again and again to maintain this new normal.

For those of you reading this book, if you have a loved one with a mental health diagnosis be encouraged to make the proper adjustments and to set realistic expectations for your family and your loved one. Making these adjustments helps you embrace the present and prepare for the future. These adjustments also allow you to let go of the pressure of living life the way it used to be and to living according to the standard of the past. This gives you the courage and hope to take heart in knowing that you can live in peace *now* even in the midst of some broken pieces.

THERE IS
HOPE

Concluding Thoughts:
A Word from Our Author
&
Clinical Consultant

The first person accounts in this book aim to offer hope, validation, and support to everyone who has a loved one with a mental health diagnosis. It provides fundamental information on some of the different symptoms and treatment options available to those with psychological concerns and their families. However, this book is not a full account of the nuances and differences that exist across clinical mental health diagnoses. Each diagnosis contains its own set of symptoms, causal factors, and treatment approaches. In addition, each individual has a unique subjective experience associated with his/her diagnosis. Therefore, the information in this book is not a "one size fits all" account or approach to understanding the complexities of mental illness. We encourage families to seek support from trained psychological and medical professionals concerning their loved one's unique diagnosis and symptom presentation.

About the Author

Teresa A. Tate is a forward-thinking leader with over 15 years' experience in the high-tech industry in Silicon Valley, California; 10 years' experience as a licensed real estate salesperson in the state of California; 15+ years' experience as a lead consultant for Wyse Solutions & Associates; and co-founder and lead pastor of Kingdom Worship Center International (KWCI). Her community and business acumen also spans several initiatives and community-based feeding programs. Her entrepreneurial and philanthropic spirit has fueled positive social and economic impact across diverse communities in the Northern California Bay Area. Her other significant accolades include work as an acclaimed certified professional life coach, a highly sought after motivational and conference speaker, #1 Best-Selling Author on Amazon, and inspirational songwriter and playwright. Her life's passion is to help individuals from all backgrounds and lifestyles to "*profitably increase and become their best selves.*" Those close to her know that her sons, Richard and Davonte (aka her "two heartbeats"), are what "fuels her WHY."

About the Collaborators

Billie Davis received her degree in nursing from Clayton State University in Morrow, Georgia. With expertise working with renal patients, Billie has worked in the medical field for 45 years. She strives to make sure her patients are well-informed and provided with expert care. She is the proud mother of three children, six grandchildren, and one great-grandchild.

Reverend Donna Edward is President and CEO of *The Godly Girls Network*, a global, high impact non-profit organization that supports women to live their best lives with victory and accomplishment. *The Godly Girls Network* also spearheads innovative and timely initiatives, like Families Against Child Trafficking (F.A.C.T.). Reverend Edward is the Founder of Kingdom Worship International – a Fellowship of Churches – and the host of God's Triumphant Girl weekly television broadcast. Reverend Edward is a forward-thinking certified Life Guide Coach who uses her 25+ years of experience as a community leader, visionary, and entrepreneur to equip and empower people from diverse backgrounds to develop a "winner's mentality." Reverend Edward is also a multifaceted corporate recruiter for the largest, private non-profit mental health provider in Santa Clara County, California. She is a humanitarian, #1 Best Selling Author on Amazon.com. She resides in San Jose, California with her husband, Pastor Robert L. Edward, Jr.

Darlena Mays is a Marketing Administrative Coordinator, and the proud CEO of DRM Food Management and Jon Jon's BBQ in San Jose, California. As a passionate supporter of women in business, she has attended the California Program for Entrepreneurship (CAPE) at the Leavey School of Business at Santa Clara University, where she also placed 1st in her food category. In addition, as a survivor of childhood molestation, Darlena truly desires to help hurting children. She held a license as a foster parent in Santa Clara County where she fostered children, served as a legal guardian, and even adopted. Further, in 2015, Darlena's new life's purpose emerged as an advocate against cancer. In July 2015, she was diagnosed with Stage 3C Uterine Cancer. After the successful completion of chemotherapy and internal & external radiation at the Cancer Treatment Center of America in Phoenix, Arizona, life seemingly returned to normal. Yet, on May 24th, 2018 she received the call that her cancer had returned in her right breast. Now a two-time cancer survivor, Darlena has used her voice to speak about her journey at multiple cancer awareness engagements. She credits God, her family, her close friend Ruth (Nurse), and a host of loved ones who were #TeamDarlena and helped pull her through. Darlena is a wife, mother, grandmother, and ministry leader and supporter who is determined to stand in the midst of every obstacle.

Valerie Watson-Smith received her Bachelor of Arts in Social Welfare (minor in Journalism) from Fresno State University located in California. Because of her expertise in social welfare, she served as a supervisor and child advocate for the Child Abuse Prevention Program at Rape Counseling Services, Inc. in Fresno, California. In this role, Valerie worked with women and children who were survivors of sexual abuse and neglect. After relocating to the Northern California Bay Area, she became a leading technical recruiter responsible for placing and hiring high-tech engineers and professionals. With over 18 years' experience, Valerie has emerged as a seasoned and reputable consultant for top-tier computer software companies. She is a self-proclaimed "tech enthusiast" who loves to match people with their dream job. Yet, her passion and love for helping people, especially women and girls, in the domains of social welfare persist. She is an active mentor and community teacher who is committed to fostering women's and young girls' positive self-esteem, empowerment, and mental, physical, and spiritual wellness through workshops. Whether it's in her role as a recruiter, community leader, or mentor, Valerie believes in helping people win! She is also the proud wife of Valentino Smith and mother to Natalie.

About the Clinical Consultant

Dr. Natalie Watson-Singleton is a mental health expert and renowned speaker, researcher, and clinician. She received her PhD in Clinical-Community psychology from the University of Illinois, Urbana-Champaign. She is currently a faculty member in the Department of Psychology at Spelman College in Atlanta, Georgia. She is also an affiliated faculty member with the Nia Project, Emory University Department of Psychiatry and Behavioral Sciences. Dr. Watson-Singleton has a wealth of knowledge and practice providing individual and group therapy to diverse adults with a range of mental health disorders. Because of this, she is a heavily sought after speaker, with invited talks geared towards equipping professionals and community members alike with practical tools to enhance their personal mental health as well as the health and wellness of their communities. Dr. Watson-Singleton is also a highly published and active researcher who investigates the effect of race, gender, and socioeconomic status on psychological help-seeking attitudes, behaviors, and health outcomes as well as ways to tailor interventions to address the mental health needs of diverse communities.

Resource List

The following list provides information on a subset of national and federal organizations aimed towards mental health support and recovery. The content reflected by each organization is solely the responsibility of that organization and does not necessarily represent the official views of the authors, collaborators, clinical consultant, and publisher. In addition, this list does not represent a formal endorsement of these organizations by the collaborative book team. We encourage each reader to seek individualized support from trained professionals concerning questions related to mental illness.

General Mental Health Support

- The U.S. Department of Health and Human Resources will provide a listing of free clinics in your area once you enter in your geographic location: https://findahealthcenter.hrsa.gov/
- The National Alliance on Mental Illness (NAMI) is a nationwide organization that provides information, resources, peer support, and groups to individuals and families affected by mental illness. Call them toll free at 1-800-950-NAMI or contact at: https://www.nami.org/
- Individuals can receive discounted individual and group therapy through training clinics, which are typically associated with universities in the region. At training clinics, graduate students provide clinical care under the supervision of a licensed psychologist. To find a

training clinic near year, go to:
https://www.aptc.org/?module=Members&event=Clinics
- Emergency Medical Services—911; If you experience a potentially life-threatening, seek immediate emergency assistance by calling 911, available 24 hours a day.

Psychiatric Medication Assistance

- The Partnership for Prescription Assistance will help you find free clinics in your area. Call their toll free number: 1-888-477-2669 or type in your zip code at the following website to find clinics in your area: https://www.pparx.org/prescription_assistance_program s/free_clinic_finder
- Assistance for medication management may be acquired at: https://www.needymeds.org/drug_list.taf
- Additional information on medication assistance can be obtained from Mental Health America at: http://www.mentalhealthamerica.net/prescription-assistance

Suicide Support and Prevention

- Groups for people grieving someone who died by suicide hosted by the American Foundation for Suicide Prevention website: afsp.org
- If you or someone you love is thinking about suicide, call the National Suicide Prevention Lifeline at 1-800-273-8255 or Text TALK to 741741 to text with a trained crisis counselor from the Crisis Text Line for free, 24/7
- To receive support for self-harming, learn more at dailystrength.org/group/self-injury.

Depression and Anxiety Support

- To obtain in-person or online support for Depression and Bipolar Disorder, visit: dbsalliance.org
- The Postpartum Progress site provides information for support groups in nearly every state as well as in Canada. To learn more at: postpartumprogress.com
- Find a state-by-state list of in-person support groups for Depression and Anxiety at the Anxiety and Depression Association of America's website: adaa.org.
- To connect with people with anxiety online, create your own profile at Anxiety Social Net: anxietysocialnet.com
- If you need support for Obsessive-Compulsive thoughts and behaviors, the International OCD Foundation lists more than 200 groups on their website: iocdf.org

Schizophrenia Support and Prevention

- The Schizophrenia and Related Disorders Alliance of America facilitates groups nationwide. To learn more, visit: sardaa.org. You can also dial into its phone groups at 1-855-640-8271 at 7 P.M. ET on Sundays, Thursdays, and Fridays with the pass code: 88286491#.
- Additional information and resources for families and individuals with schizophrenia can be obtained from the National Institute of Mental Health (NIMH) at: https://www.nimh.nih.gov/health/topics/schizophrenia/raise/raise-resources-for-patients-and-families.shtml

Substance Use and Addiction Support and Prevention

- To receive general information and to locate treatment services in your area, you can call the Substance Abuse and Mental Health Services Administration (SAMHSA) Treatment Referral Helpline at: 1-877-SAMHSA7 (1-877-726-4727). A live person will be available to speak to you, Monday through Friday from 8 a.m. to 8 p.m. EST.

- If you are an adult child of a parent with alcoholism, the Adult Children of Alcoholics World Service Organization maintains numerous support groups and hosts call-in and online sessions at: meetings.adultchildren.org

References

[1] Mental illness. *Mayo Clinic*. Retrieved from http://www.mayoclinic.org/diseases-conditions/mental-illness/basics/definition/con-20033813

[2] Mental illness. *National Institute of Mental Illness*. Retrieved from http://www.nimh.nih.gov/health/statistics/prevalence/any-mental-illness-ami-among-adults.shtml

[3] The state of mental health in America: Mental health facts, stats, and data. *Mental Health America*. Retrieved from http://www.mentalhealthamerica.net/issues/state-mental-health-america

[4] The state of mental health in America: Mental health facts, stats, and data. *Mental Health America*. Retrieved from http://www.mentalhealthamerica.net/issues/state-mental-health-america

[5] Amadeo, K. (2019, January 24). Deinstitutionalization, its causes, effects, pros, and cons: How deinstitutionalization in the 1970s affects you today. *Balance*. Retrieved from https://www.thebalance.com/deinstitutionalization-3306067

[6] Alasko, C. (2012, April 23). How does denial actually work? *Psychology Today*. Retrieved from https://www.psychologytoday.com/us/blog/beyond-blame/201204/how-does-denial-actually-work

[7] Mental illness. *National Institute of Mental Illness*. Retrieved from http://www.nimh.nih.gov/health/statistics/prevalence/any-mental-illness-ami-among-adults.shtml

[8] Kraus Whitbourne, S. (2015, September 19). Five reasons we play the blame game…but rarely win. *Psychology Today*. Retrieved from https://www.psychologytoday.com/us/blog/fulfillment-any-age/201509/5-reasons-we-play-the-blame-game

[9] Seltzer, L.F. (2015, January 14). Don't let your anger "mature" into bitterness: Bitterness, its cause, cost, and cure. *Psychology Today*. Retrieved from

https://www.psychologytoday.com/us/blog/evolution-the-self/201501/don-t-let-your-anger-mature-bitterness

[10] Caregiver stress and burnout: Tips for regaining your energy optimism, and hope. *HelpGuide*. Retrieved from https://www.helpguide.org/articles/stress/caregiver-stress-and-burnout.htm

[11] Iseselo, Kajula & Yahya-Malima (2015). The psychosocial problems of families caring for relatives with mental illnesses and their coping strategies: A qualitative urban based study in Dar es Salaam, Tanzania, *BMC Psychiatry, 16,* 146.

[12] Dowd, C. (2014). The financial implications of being a caregiver. *Fox Business*. Retrieved from http://www.foxbusiness.com/features/2014/09/18/financial-implications-being-caregiver.html

[13] Caregiver stress and burnout: Tips for regaining your energy optimism, and hope. *HelpGuide*. Retrieved from https://www.helpguide.org/articles/stress/caregiver-stress-and-burnout.htm

[14] Dowd, C. (2014). The financial implications of being a caregiver. *Fox Business*. Retrieved from http://www.foxbusiness.com/features/2014/09/18/financial-implications-being-caregiver.html

[15] Bourg Carter, S. (2013, November 26). The tell take signs of burnout: Do you have them? *Psychology Today*. Retrieved from https://www.psychologytoday.com/us/blog/high-octane-women/201311/the-tell-tale-signs-burnout-do-you-have-them

[16] Does mental health affect and impinge on family relationships? *Priory*. Retrieved from https://www.priorygroup.com/blog/does-mental-health-affect-and-impinge-on-family-relationships

[17] Neff, K. (2011). *Self-compassion: The proven power of being kind to yourself.* New York, New York. William Morrow.

[18] Morrow, A. (2018, May 16). Differences between normal and complication grief. *Very Well Health*. Retrieved from https://www.verywellhealth.com/grief-and-mourning-process-1132545

[19] Hospitalization. *Mental Health America*. Retrieved from http://www.mentalhealthamerica.net/hospitalization

[20] Preventing relapse of mental illnesses. *Here to Help*. Retrieved from http://www.heretohelp.bc.ca/factsheet/preventing-relapse-of-mental-illnesses

[21] Tartakovsky, M. (2016). Fifteen ways to support a loved one with serious mental illness. *Psych Central*. Retrieved from https://psychcentral.com/lib/15-ways-to-support-a-loved-one-with-serious-mental-illness/

[22] Relapse and relapse prevention. *Encyclopedia of Mental Disorders*. Retrieved from http://www.minddisorders.com/Py-Z/Relapse-and-relapse-prevention.html#ixzz4jnJykbnn

[23] Schizophrenia and schizophrenia facts. *Schizophrenia.com*. Retrieved from http://www.schizophrenia.com/szfacts.htm#

[24] Burton, N. (2012). Mental illness: Preventing a relapse. *Psychology Today*. Retrieved from https://www.psychologytoday.com/blog/hide-and-seek/201210/mental-illness-preventing-relapse

[25] Preventing relapse of mental illnesses. *Here to Help*. Retrieved from http://www.heretohelp.bc.ca/factsheet/preventing-relapse-of-mental-illnesses

[26] Preventing relapse of mental illnesses. *Here to Help*. Retrieved from http://www.heretohelp.bc.ca/factsheet/preventing-relapse-of-mental-illnesses

[27] Mental illness. *Mayo Clinic*. Retrieved from http://www.mayoclinic.org/diseases-conditions/mental-illness/basics/definition/con-20033813

[28] The myth of violence and mental illness. *Canadian Mental Health Association*. Retrieved from https://cmhadurham.ca/finding-help/the-myth-of-violence-and-mental-illness/

[29] Pescosolido, B.A., Jensen, P.S., Martin, J.K., Perry, B.L., Olafsdottir, S., & Fettes, D. (2008). Public knowledge and assessment of child mental health problems: Findings from the

National Stigma Study—Children. *Journal of the American Academy of Child & Adolescent Psychiatry, 47,* 339–349.

[30] Corrigan, P.W., & Watson, A. (2002). Understanding the impact of stigma on people with mental illness. *World Psychiatry, 1*(1), 16-20.

[31] Corrigan, P.W., & Watson, A. (2002). Understanding the impact of stigma on people with mental illness. *World Psychiatry, 1*(1), 16-20.

[32] Corrigan, P.W., & Kleinlein, P. (2005). The impact of mental illness stigma. In Corrigan, P.W. (Ed.), *On the Stigma of Mental Illness: Implications for Research and Social Change.* Washington: The American Psychological Association.

[33] Hyman, S.E. (2000). The genetics of mental illness: Implications for practice. Bulletin of the World Health Organization, 78(4), 455-463.

[34] Shibre, T. et al. (2001). Perception of stigma among family members of individuals with schizophrenia and major affective disorders in rural Ethiopia. *Social Psychiatry and Psychiatric Epidemiology, 36*(6), 299-303.

[35] Corrigan, P.W. et al. (2001). Three strategies for changing attributions about severe mental illness. *Schizophrenia Bulletin, 27*(2), 187-195.

[36] Simpson, A. (n.d.). Mental illness: What is the church's role? *Christianity Today.* Retrieved from http://qideas.org/articles/mental-illness-what-is-the-churchs-role/

[37] Funaro, V. (n.d.) Rick Warren on mental illness: 'If my brain doesn't work and I take a pill, I'm supposed to be ashamed?' *Christian Post.* Retrieved from http://www.christianpost.com/news/rick-warren-on-mental-illness-if-my-brain-doesnt-work-and-i-take-a-pill-im-supposed-to-be-ashamed-119628/

[38] Banks, A.M. (n.d.). Rick Warren to pastors: 'There is no testimony without a test.' *The Washington Post.* Retrieved from https://www.washingtonpost.com/national/religion/rick-warren-to-pastors-there-is-no-testimony-without-a-test/2014/06/10/4fbd256c-f0b8-11e3-85d2-cda8aebfefe0_story.html?utm_term=.e14f904fbe86

[39] American Psychological Association (n.d.) *How to cope when a loved one has a serious mental illness*. Retrieved from https://www.apa.org/helpcenter/serious-mental-illness
[40] Mills, H. (n.d.). *What is anger?* Retrieved from https://www.mentalhelp.net/articles/what-is-anger/

TO OUR SPONSORS

We appreciate your generous support
while helping us share a message of hope.

TO OUR READERS

It is our sincere hope that you will benefit from
the resources offered in the next section.

Answer The Call To Fulfill Kingdom Purpose

KINGDOM WORSHIP INTERNATIONAL FELLOWSHIP OF CHURCHES

Our only requirement is that you *live* a
Christ-Centered life, have Kingdom Focus
and a desire to make Kingdom Impact.

Our Purpose & Vision

We exist to provide a Christ-Centered
Non-denominational fellowship that
will encourage, edify, educate and empower
Ministry/Marketplace Leaders, Ministries and
Churches while providing opportunity for those
seeking Kingdom fellowship, networking and
spiritual support.

Contact Overseer Rev. Donna Edward

KWIFOC@outlook.com
Facebook @KWIFOC
408-5420-KWI

HAVE YOU HEARD THE WORD?

THERE'S A NEW
CHURCH

IN TOWN BUILDING PEOPLE
AND FAMILIES BY PROMOTING
KINGDOM PURPOSE & BUSINESS

LEAD BY SENIOR PASTOR TERESA TATE

KINGDOM WORSHIP
CENTER INTERNATIONAL
JOIN SUNDAY AT 10:30 AM
& WEDNESDAY AT 7:00 PM

234 E. GISH ROAD, SUITE 300. SAN JOSE CA 95112

FACEBOOK.COM/KWCICHURCH

WHO WE ARE

WOMEN RISING ABOVE ABUSE IS A NONPROFIT COMMUNITY LOOKING TO HELP WOMEN OVERCOME ABUSE IN ALL FORMS.

MISSION

Our Mission at WRAA is to help women And girls who have suffered unresolved hurt and trauma caused by sexual, emotional, and physical abuse heal both spiritually and naturally. We provide a safe environment and help these women and girls move from a life of hopelessness to a life empowerment through Love.
We want to give them tools necessary to succeed, and to move forward with a renewed spirit.

Women Rising Above Abuse

I'm not ashamed of my past.
The decisions
I made good or bad I own.
They made me the women I am today. I may have fallen, but out of those trials arose a STRONG, CONFIDENT women
who knows who
She is. You cannot break me.
I will always rise above!

WOMEN RISING ABOVE ABUSE
3155 San Felipe Rd #97
San Jose, Ca 95135
email: info@womennrisingaboveabuse.org
phone: 408.189.8672

www.womenrisingaboveabuse.org

WOMEN RISING ABOVE ABUSE

Women Rising Above Abuse

BREAK THE SILENCE

PHYSICAL ABUSE

Physical abuse is the most visible form of abuse and may be defined as any act that results in a non-accidental trauma or physical injury.

- The longer the abuse continues, the more serious the injuries to the person and the ore difficult it is to eliminate the abusive behavior.

SEXUAL ABUSE

Sexual abuse is any sort of non consensual sexual contact. Sexual abuse by a partner/intimate can include derogatory name calling, refusal to use contraception, deliberately causing unwanted physical pain during sex, deliberately passing on sexual diseases or infections and using objects, toys, or other items (e.g. baby oil or lubricants) without consent and to cause pain or humiliation.

CHILD SEXUAL ABUSE

- Sexual toching of any part of the body, clothed or unclothed;
- Penetrative sex, including penetration of the mouth;
- Encouraging a child to engage in sexual activity, including masturbation;
- Intentionally engaging in sexual activity in front of a child;
- Showing children pornography, or using children to create pornography;
- Encouraging a child to engage in prostitution.

FORMS OF ABUSE

Emotional Abuse, Physical Abuse sexual Abuse

EMOTIONAL ABUSE

Happen when someone insults, humiliates or uses "to control another person. It can happen to people in all income, education, and ethnic groups.

Emotional Abuse doesn't always lead to physical violence however almost all physical or sexual abuse includes emotional abuse. Being emotionally abused puts a person at risk of physical abuse.

Emotional Abuse is Hard to Recognize
- The abused person may not ever realize it's happening
- This can make it hard to take steps to stop it
- The longer the abuse goes on, the more harmful it can be.

WHY WOMEN RISING ABOVE ABUSE?

I started Women Rising Above Abuse because I know our community is need of it. As a child, I was molested and raped. During that time of my life I had no outlet, nor was there any program that we knew of that could help me through those trying times. I wanted to be delivered and healed from those past hurts, yet I found myself in emotionally and physically abusive relationships as time went on. Today, I am an overcomer, empowered, and strengthen. I am no longer a victim of my past hurts or traumas. I want to help young girls and women become overcomers themselves. This my calling and what I desire to do, in 1 Thessalonians 5:1 I (KJV) It says; Therefore, encourage and comfort one another and build up one another. Just as you are doing. We should not have to live our lives in fear or shame but, in peace and joy.

You are special, you are worth it, you will be okay

Mardan Randolph
Executive Director

God is in the midst of her, she shall not be moved; God shall help her, just at the break of dawn." Psalms 46:5 NKJV

Emotional Abuse: 1.800.621.HOPE (4673)
Sexual Abuse: 1.800.656.4673
Physical Abuse: 1.800.799.SAFE (7233)

How to get Help.
If you are a sexual abuse survivor, or you think you may have been a victim of sexual abuse, peer support can be very helpful. Remember that it was not your fault.